BODY

David Lambert

The Diagram Group

HarperCollins*Publishers*

HarperCollins Publishers
P.O. Box, Glasgow G4 0NB

A Diagram Book first created by Diagram Visual Information Limited of 195 Kentish Town Road, London NW5 8SY, England

First published 1991
© Diagram Visual Information Limited 1991
Reprint 10 9 8 7 6 5 4 3 2 1

ISBN 0 00 458953 X
All rights reserved

Printed in Great Britain by
HarperCollins Manufacturing, Glasgow

Introduction

This pocket guide offers a visual and wide-ranging user's manual for all human-body owners. Each chapter contains headings followed by brief sections explaining basic facts about the body as simply as possible. Text is closely integrated with clearly labelled diagrams, charts, maps, and other visual aids.

Chapter 1 (**Body in perspective**) is a broad overview of the human body – its ingredients, origins, variety of types, and range of life expectancies.

Chapter 2 (**Body systems**) explores the body's bony scaffolding, muscular machinery, heart–lung system, digestive system, control centres, and other parts all synchronized to keep the body working properly.

Chapter 3 (**Starting life**) traces life from conception to birth and beyond: through a child's physical, mental, and psychological development.

Chapter 4 (**Staying healthy**) looks at the body's needs for food, exercise, personal hygiene, sleep and other factors that can help to keep us not just well but fit from day to day.

Chapter 5 (**When things go wrong**) deals with disease and injury and how natural defences and modern medicine can often prevent or overcome such problems.

Chapter 6 (**The aging body**) shows how bodies change with age, the problems aging brings, some ways of keeping age at bay, and remarkable achievements accomplished by famous over 40s.

Contents

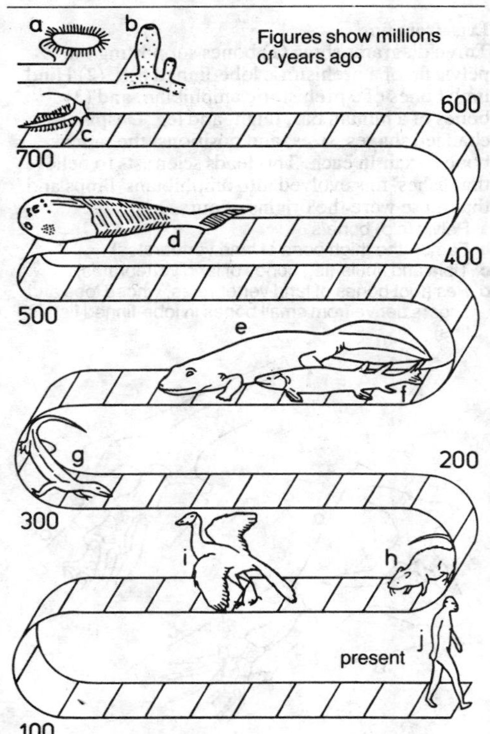
a
b
Figures show millions of years ago
c
600
700
d
400
500
e
f
g
200
300
i
h
j
present
100

Legs from fins

Three diagrams show (**1**) bones supporting the pelvic fin of a prehistoric lobe-finned fish, (**2**) Hind limb bones of a prehistoric amphibian, and (**3**) bones of a human hip, thigh, and leg. Despite changed shapes, sizes, and positions, the same key bones occur in each. This leads scientists to believe that fishes' fins evolved into amphibians' limbs and that these were the origins of ours.

a Pelvic (hip) bone/s
b Femur (the thigh bone of land vertebrates)
c Tibia and fibula (leg bones of land vertebrates)
d Pes (foot bones of land vertebrates, whose toes and fingers derive from small bones in lobe-finned fishes' fins)

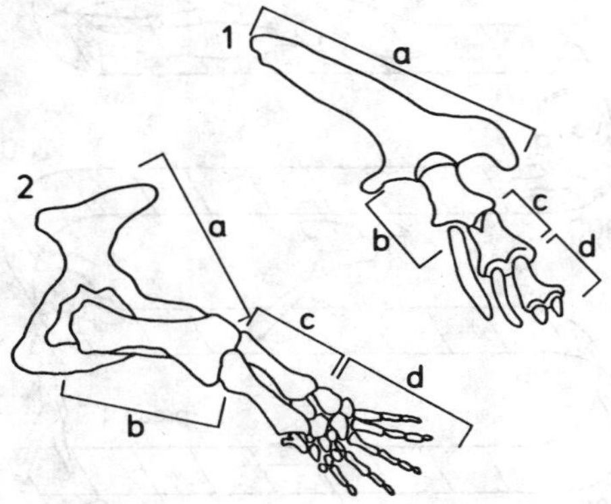

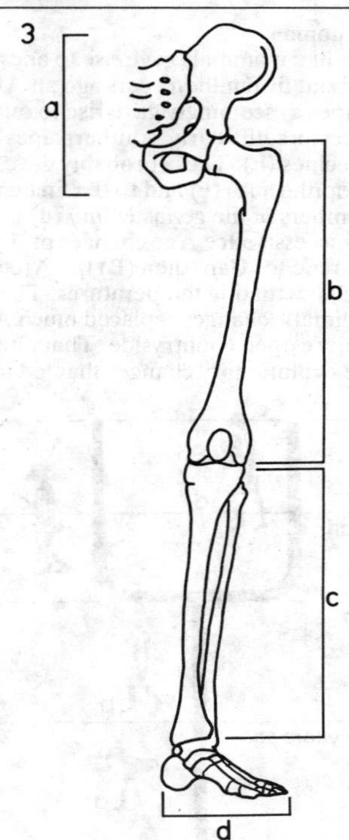
3
a
b
c
d

From ape to human

Small mouse-like mammals gave rise to apes and monkeys. About five million years ago an African prehistoric ape (**a**) seemingly gave rise to our ape-man ancestors, the early 'southern apes' or australopithecines (**b**). These probably gave rise to later australopithecines (**c**) and to the first true humans: members of the genus *Homo* (**d**). Meanwhile successive Ice Age changes produced (**A**) the Antarctic Ice Cap, then (**B**) the Arctic Ice Cap, then (**C**) fluctuating temperatures. These worldwide climatic changes replaced much African forest with more open countryside. That alteration favoured the evolutionary changes that led to humans.

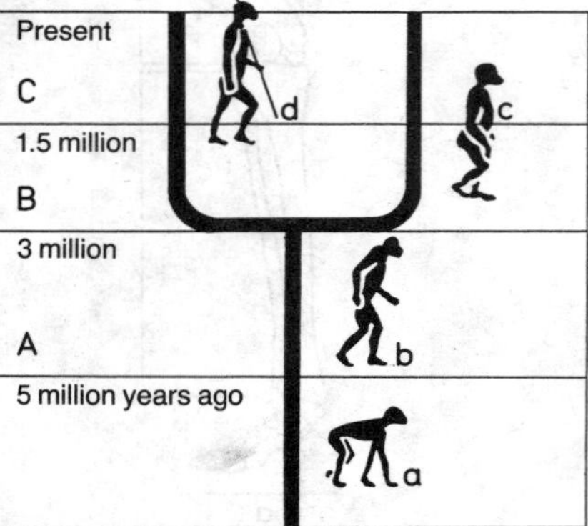

Hominization

Ape men, adapting from forest life to grassland life, faced increased risk from predators but increased food supplies from big meaty herbivores. Grassland life probably involved the self-reinforcing changes of hominization: the making of mankind.

a Groups needed to co-operate to survive
b Group ties were strengthened by a home base where food was shared
c Making and using tools favoured hand-eye co-ordination and bipedal walking
d Evolving brains improved tool-making methods and communication
e A long childhood period of care and learning improved the chances of survival

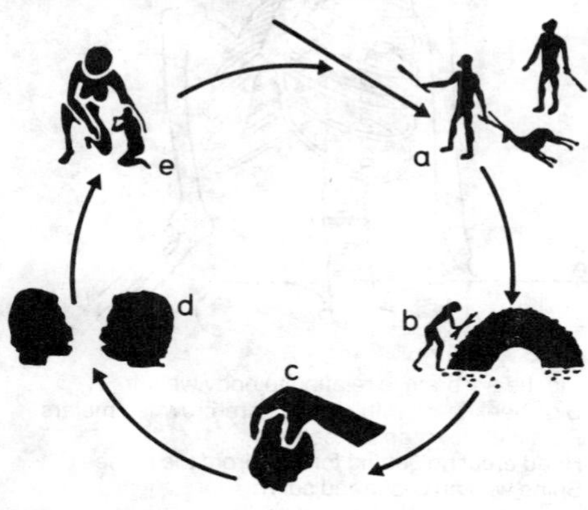

The human tribe

Some scientists lump together man and the australopithecines as hominines, the human tribe. Key features collectively distinguish it from apes.

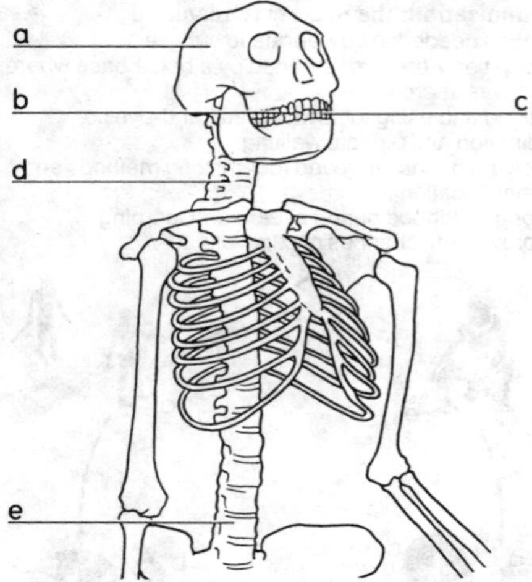

a Big, heavy brain in relation to body weight
b Big cheek teeth with high square-crowned molars
c Relatively low canine teeth
d Head erect not jutting forward from the spine
e Spine with an S-shaped curve

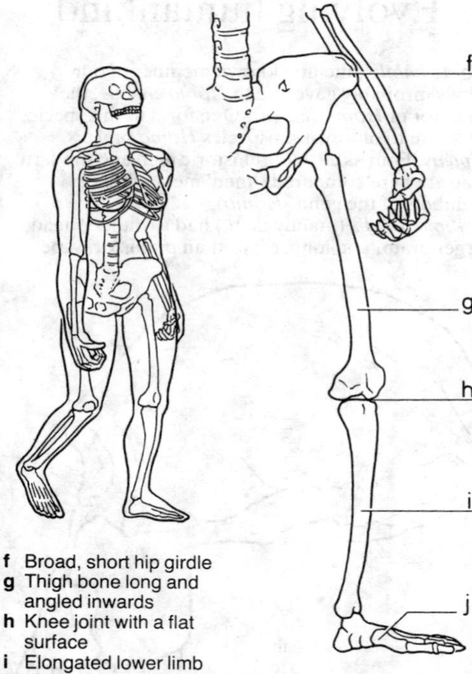

f Broad, short hip girdle
g Thigh bone long and angled inwards
h Knee joint with a flat surface
i Elongated lower limb
j 'Platform' shaped foot

Evolving humankind

Homo habilis, the first known member of our genus, probably gave rise to *Homo erectus*, the ancestor of *Homo sapiens*. One form of this species gave rise to our own subspecies *Homo sapiens sapiens*. Four skulls of prehistoric men and modern man are here compared ('men' meaning simply members of the genus *Homo*).

1 *Homo habilis* ('handy man') had a rounder head, larger brain, and longer face than prehistoric ape

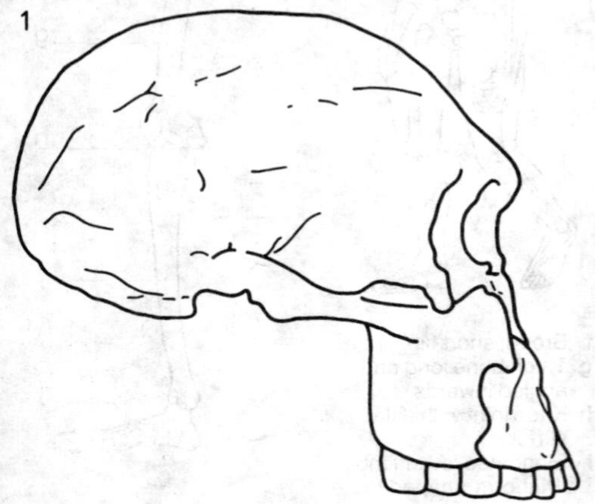

men, but relatively longer arms than ours. Height: 1.2–1.5m (4–5ft). Brain capacity: 650–800cc. Time: 2–1.5 million years ago.

2 *Homo erectus* ('upright man') had a bigger body and brain than its likely ancestor *Homo habilis*, but a long, low skull with brow ridges and projecting chinless jaws. Height: 1.5–1.8m (5–6ft). Brain capacity: 880–1100cc. Time: 1.6 million–200,000 years ago.

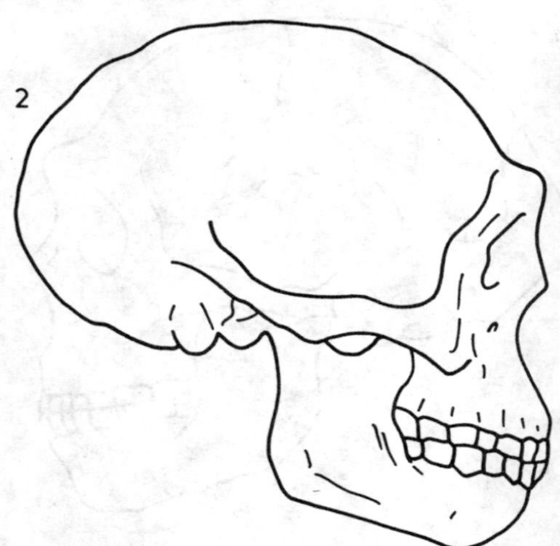

3 *Homo sapiens neanderthalensis* ('Neanderthal man'), an early member of our species, was short and stocky, with a big brain, large, long head, and strong chinless jaws. Most scientists suppose Neanderthals were not our ancestors but a dead-end offshoot from the line that led to fully modern man. Height: about 1.7m (5.6ft). Brain capacity: 1500cc. Time: 200,000–30,000 years ago.

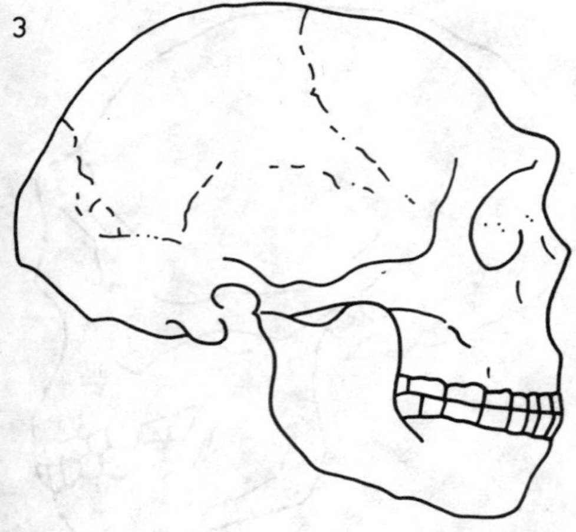

4 *Homo sapiens sapiens* ('wise man') has a tall, short head with a rounded braincase and a chin but slight or no brow ridges. Early European forms were taller but more slightly built than the Neanderthals and probably evolved from some other early form of *Homo sapiens* living probably in Africa. Height: 1.6–1.8m (5ft 4in–6ft). Brain capacity: 1400cc. Time: From 40,000 years ago until today.

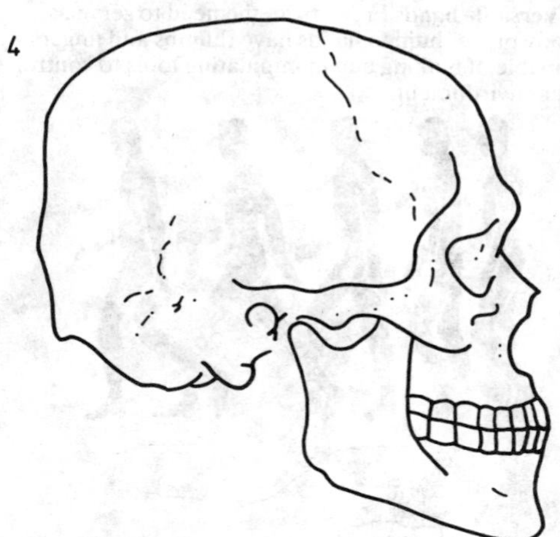

Human animal comparisons

The human body consists of chemicals also found in other creatures. Yet four developments collectively give us an advantage over all of these.

1 Bipedal walking Thanks to an upright skeleton, we walk on two legs, with a heel-toe action.

2 Versatile hands Freed from the need to serve as body props, human hands have thumbs and fingers capable of making and manipulating tools to control our environment.

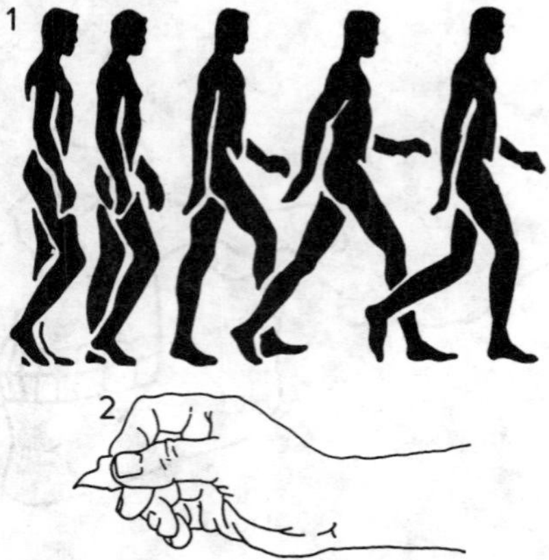

3 Binocular colour vision Forward-facing eyes can sharply focus images of objects near or far.
4 Complex brain Large for body size and with a huge surface area, our deeply wrinkled brain is uniquely capable of learning, thinking, controlling speech, and co-ordinating hand-eye actions.

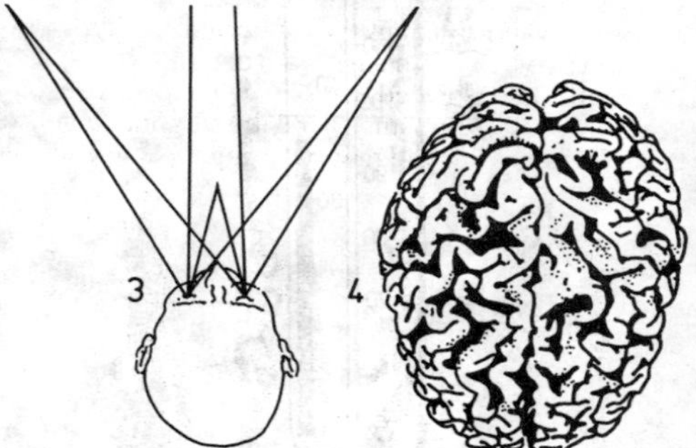

Body temperatures
Like all animals, we need heat to keep our bodies alive. Like all warm-blooded animals we have built-in thermostats to keep our body at a constant temperature. (We produce heat by burning food inside the body and store or shed body heat according to our needs.) Cold-blooded creatures' temperatures vary very much with those of their surroundings, although, like us, cold-blooded creatures' bodies have ideal temperatures at which they work best.

Here we plot normal human body temperature (**a**) against temperature range for most warm-blooded creatures (**b**) and the range of ideal temperatures for most cold-blooded creatures (**c**).

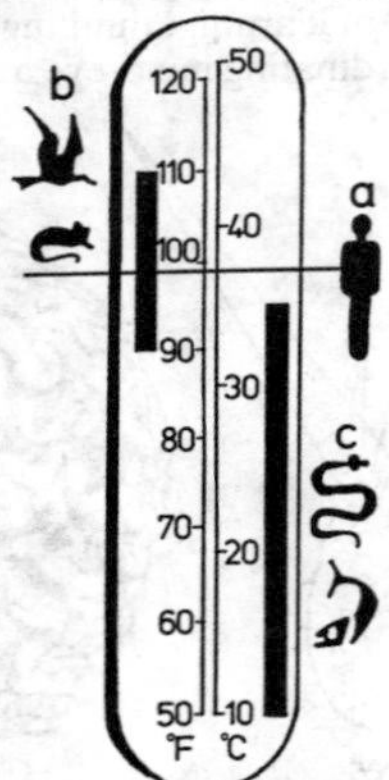

Mammals		
Goat	39.9°C	103.8°F
Domestic rabbit	38.5°C	101.3°F
Northern fur seal	37.7°C	99.9°F
Polar bear	37.3°C	99.1°F
Human	37.0°C	98.6°F
African elephant	36.4°C	97.5°F
Blue whale	35.5°C	95.9°F
Three-toed sloth	33.2°C	91.7°F
Spiny anteater	23.3°C	73.9°F

Body temperatures 2
Humans and other animals vary in the temperature extremes they can survive. Our diagram plots against a thermometer survived extremes for six kinds of animal, and man, alongside a horizontal line depicting normal human body temperature. In each group many individuals would die of hypothermia (overcooling) or hyperthermia (overheating) before they reached the extremes shown for that group.

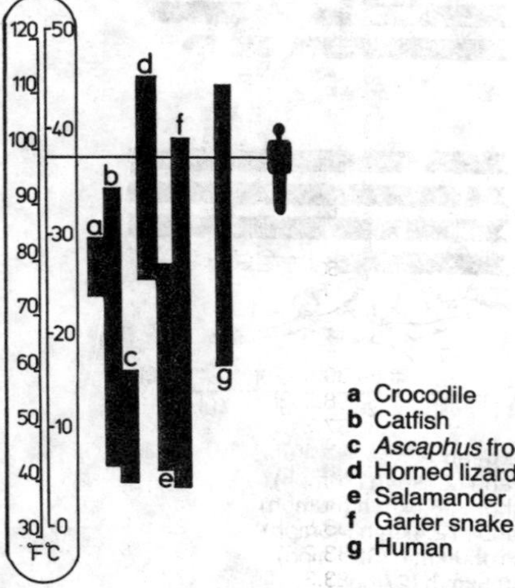

Speeds compared

Without artificial aids the human body is no match for certain other creatures when it comes to

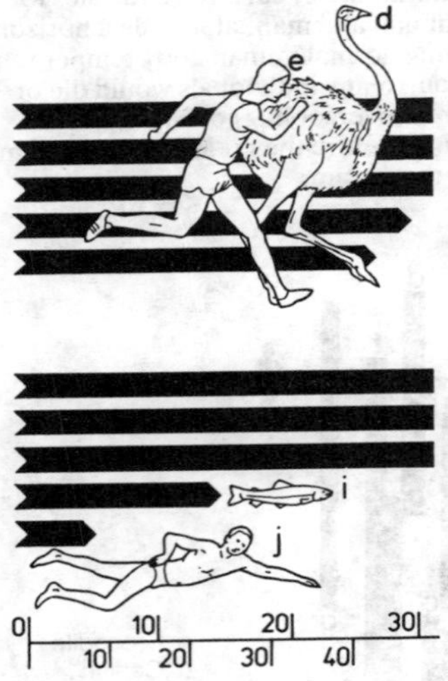

Land speeds

a Cheetah 112.7km/h (70mph)
b Pronghorn 96.6km/h (60mph)
c Jackrabbit 72.4km/h (45mph)
d Ostrich 48+km/h (30+mph)
e Man 43.5km/h (27mph)

eyesight, weapons, strength, and speed. Here we compare top human land and water speeds with those of some of nature's champions.

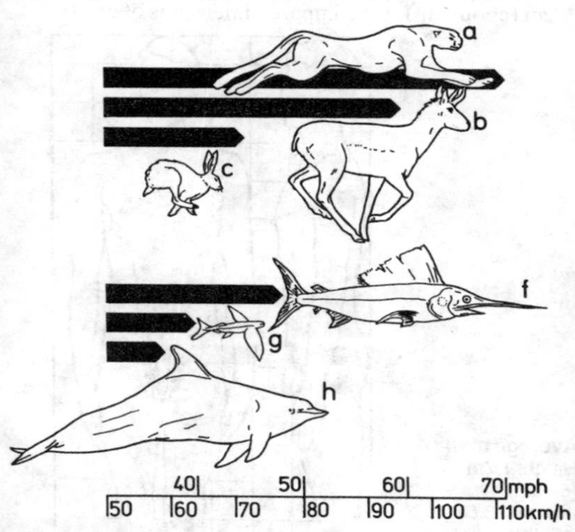

Water speeds

f Sailfish 96.6+km/h (60+mph)
g Flying fish 64.4km/h (40+mph)
h Dolphin 59.5km/h (37mph)
i Trout 24.1km/h (15mph)
j Man 8.4km/h (5.2mph)

Body sizes and shapes

Plotted on a grid where each side of each square is 10cm (about 4in), we compare dimensions of an

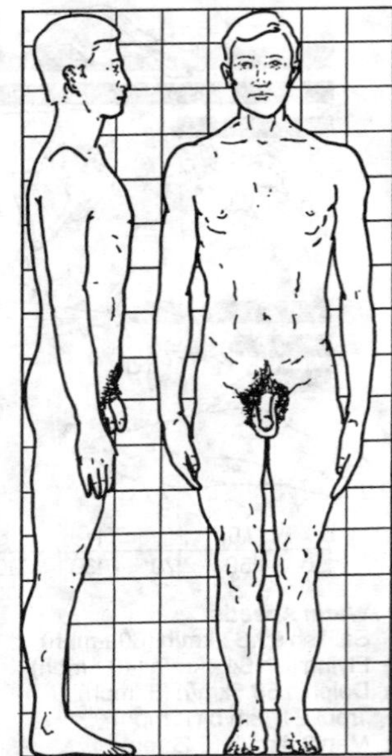

Average man
Height 1.7m
(5ft 9in)
Weight 73.5kg
(162lb)
Chest 98cm
(38.75in)
Waist 81cm
(31.75in)
Hips 96cm
(37.75in)

average man and woman (the trend is for increasing height). Males are taller than females except about the age of 12 when a girl's growth spurt puts her for a while ahead.

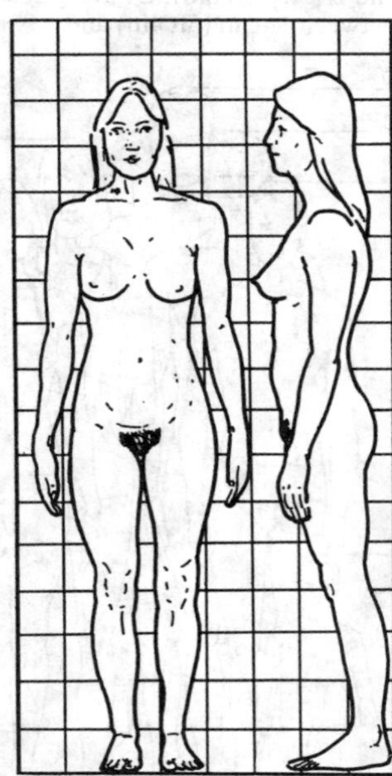

Average woman
Height 1.6m
(5ft 3.75in)
Weight 61.23kg
(135lb)
Bust 90cm
(35.5in)
Waist 74cm
(29.25in)
Hips 96cm
(38in)

Normal/abnormal height
Diagrams illustrate the relative range of heights of men and women. The normal range is small. Of every 100 women 95 stand between 1.47m (4ft 10in) and 1.73m (5ft 8in). Of every 100 men, 95 stand between 1.63m (5ft 4in) and 1.93m (6ft 2in).

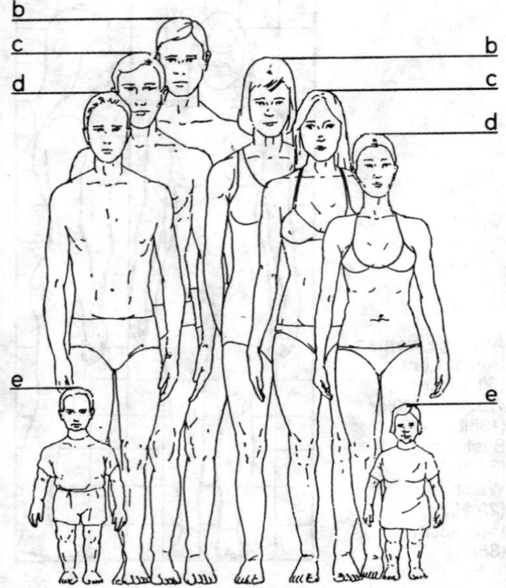

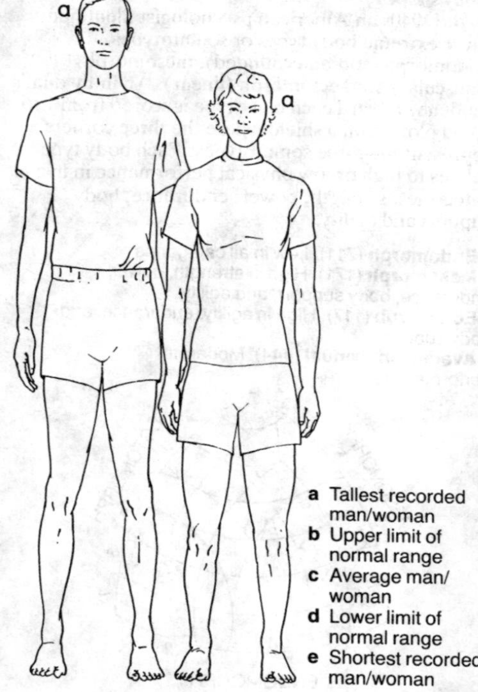

a Tallest recorded man/woman
b Upper limit of normal range
c Average man/woman
d Lower limit of normal range
e Shortest recorded man/woman

Body shapes
In the 1940s an American psychologist identified three extreme body types or somatotypes: endomorph (soft and rounded), mesomorph (muscular), and ectomorph (linear). An individual's tendency toward each body type is scored from 1 to 7 and plotted on a shield where the three corners represent the three somatotypes. Each body type relates to high or low physical performance in five categories: strength; power; endurance; body support and agility.

1 Endomorph (711). Low in all categories
2 Mesomorph (171). High in strength, power, endurance, body support, and agility.
3 Ectomorph (117). High in agility, endurance, and body support.
4 Average individual (444). Moderate performances.

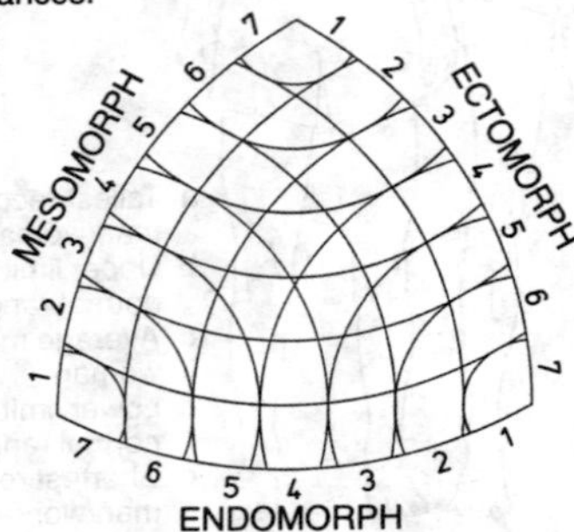

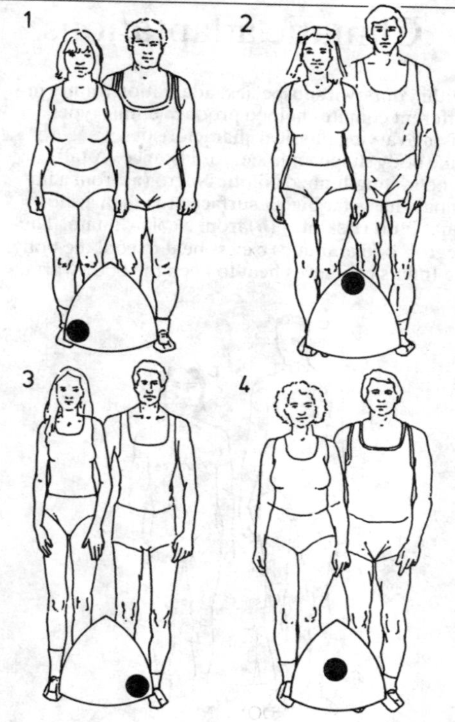
1
2
3
4

Climatic adaptations

Within our own subspecies adaptation for life in different climates helped produce ethnic types having varying physical characteristics.
Take body shape and size, for instance. A tall, slender, long-limbed Nilotic Negro (**a**) from a hot climate has a far bigger surface area than a short, squat Inuit (Eskimo) (**b**) from a cold climate. The Negro's body radiates excess heat to cool the body, the Inuit's conserves heat to keep the body warm.

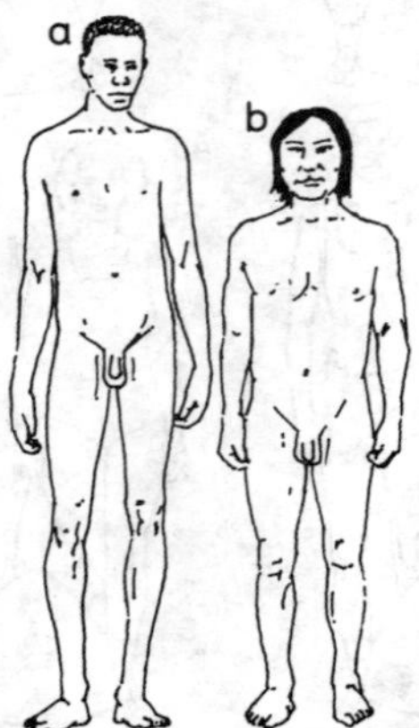

Anthropologists once recognized three major human groups based largely on skin colour. Maps show their distribution: **Caucasoid** (White), **Negroid** (Black), and **Mongoloid** (Yellow). Dark skin protects Blacks from skin cancers caused by strong tropical sunshine. Pale skin helps Whites absorb vitamin D from weak sunshine. Yellow skin reflects light well in snow or deserts. Yet Negroids range from sallow to almost black, Caucasoids from pinkish to dark brown, and Mongoloids from yellowish to white and bronze. None of the three is a true race (a biological breeding group) and the Negroid Melanesians and Negroes are unrelated. Moreover migrations now bring intermixing to ethnic groups that had evolved in isolation.

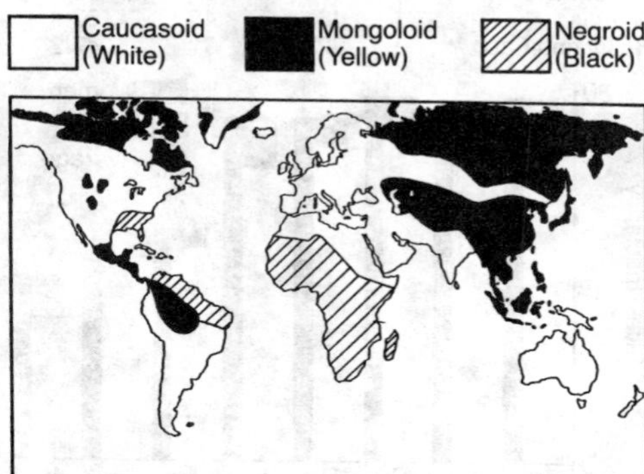

Life expectancy

The diagram below compares differences between life expectancy at birth for boys and girls recorded in the 1980s for eight countries (**A–H**) rich and poor. An average figure, based on the years 1985–1990, is also shown.

	Men 1980s	Women 1980s	Average 1985–90
A Sweden	72	78	76.8
B Japan	72	77	77.2
C USA	70	78	75.0
D UK	68	74	74.5
E USSR	64	74	72.1
F Bolivia	47	51	53.1
G India	46	45	57.9
H Burkina Faso	32	31	47.2

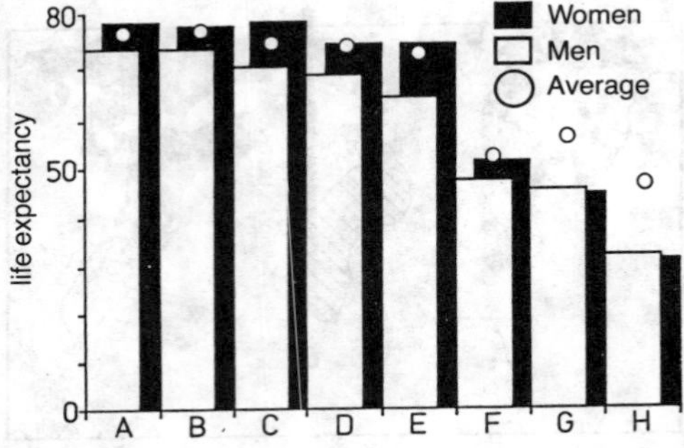

2 This diagram shows how life expectancy improves with age. In most countries women can expect a longer life than men, and people with long-lived parents are also likely to enjoy long lives.

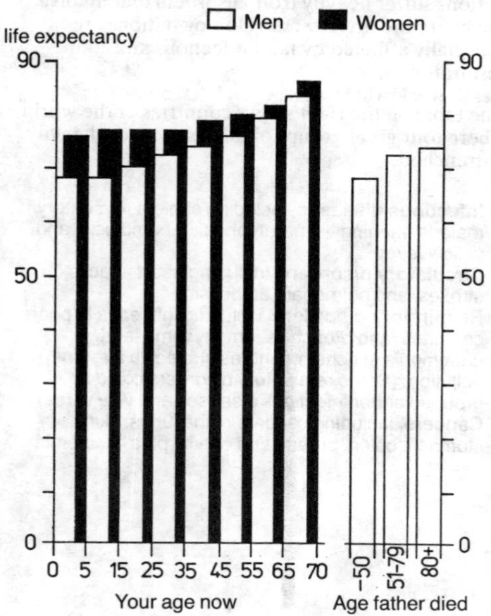

Deaths of rich and poor
In the wealthy industrially-developed nations the chief killers are different from those found in the poor developing nations of the world. Developed nations suffer heavily from disorders that involve the heart and arteries; developing nations are especially afflicted by fatal infectious and respiratory illnesses.

Death worldwide
The table on the right shows countries of the world where four great groups of killers are most heavily entrenched.

A Infectious diseases, including cholera, dysentery, malaria, meningitis, paratyphoid, tuberculosis, and yellow fever

B Circulatory disorders, including heart attacks, strokes, and pulmonary embolisms

C Respiratory disorders, including influenza in poorer countries, and bronchitis, emphysema, and pneumonia in richer countries subject to airborne pollution. (Some respiratory disorders could be grouped under infectious diseases and vice versa)

D Cancers, including cancers of the lungs, skin, stomach, colon, breast, and cervix, plus leukaemia

	A	B	C	D
	Infectious diseases	**Circulatory disorders**	**Respiratory disorders**	**Cancers**
Mauritius	14.0	336.8	90.1	88.4
Argentina	23.4	358.2	55.3	155.2
Barbados	23.2	218.4	43.3	176.2
Canada	6.1	336.6	81.1	214.8
Chile	28.0	188.3	121.3	183.7
Costa Rica	22.5	239.1	131.8	207.8
Guatemala	165.1	117.3	150.9	83.2
Guyana	18.0	158.4	68.4	67.3
USA	14.1	387.4	79.3	195.1
Venezuela	49.5	278.6	95.5	147.6
Sri Lanka	44.7	73.5	45.9	46.0
Austria	2.3	322.5	42.7	203.2
Bulgaria	4.4	301.0	60.7	112.2
Denmark	3.8	314.7	65.9	238.0
France	13.8	228.9	70.3	186.9
W Germany	6.2	330.2	48.1	216.7
Greece	5.2	302.8	56.6	137.5
Hungary	5.5	231.4	36.7	187.0
Ireland	5.9	320.3	146.1	196.0
Israel	21.8	330.6	69.9	165.5
Holland	6.1	296.4	73.9	219.4
Norway	6.9	303.7	103.7	198.7
Poland	5.0	188.9	35.4	152.1
Spain	8.2	261.2	79.0	155.0
Sweden	8.3	365.8	81.4	190.2
Switzerland	6.4	318.4	50.2	221.5
UK	4.0	293.6	102.6	222.3
Kuwait	34.7	181.3	72.5	101.7
Australia	4.7	358.3	55.1	196.2
Japan	11.3	231.4	105.2	172.9
Singapore	28.0	234.4	186.6	171.6

The body analysed

Your body contains more than one in five of the 92 chemical elements found on or in the Earth. Most are chemically combined as compounds: two-thirds of your weight is water, a compound of oxygen and hydrogen. The body's six most abundant elements include only two of the six most abundant in the Earth's crust.

Elements of the Earth's crust

Proportions by weight of the six most abundant elements in the Earth's crust. (Next come potassium, magnesium, titanium, and hydrogen.)

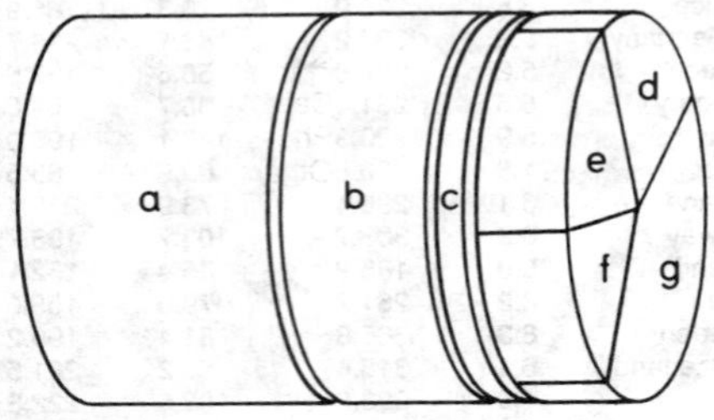

a Oxygen 46.6%
b Silicon 27.7%
c Aluminium 8.1%
d Iron 5%
e Calcium 3.6%
f Sodium 2.8%
g Others 6.2%

Elements of the body
Proportions by weight of the body's six most abundant elements. (Others include potassium, sulphur, chlorine, sodium, magnesium, iron, iodine cobalt, manganese, molybdenum, selenium, copper, zinc, chromium, and fluorine).

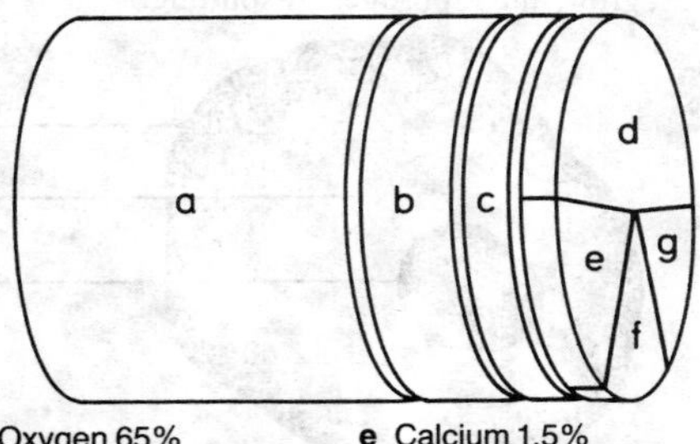

a Oxygen 65%
b Carbon 18.5%
c Hydrogen 9.5%
d Nitrogen 3.3%
e Calcium 1.5%
f Phosphorus 1%
g Others 1.2%

Cells

Elements combined as compounds build the body's basic living units: cells. About 10 million million cells go to form one human body. Each cell's main ingredients are molecules of nucleic acids, proteins, and water. Most kinds of cell harness these substances in ways that let cells take in food, shed wastes, grow, and reproduce by splitting.

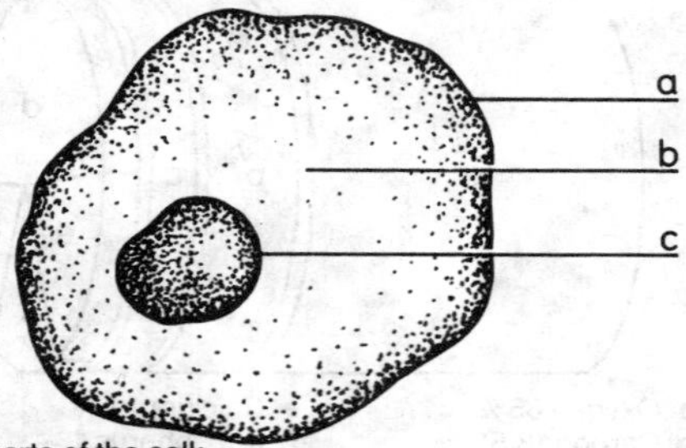

Basic parts of the cell:
a Cell membrane: an outer 'skin'.
b Cytoplasm: a transparent 'jelly'.
c Nucleus: the cell's control centre.

Tissues and organs

Similar cells that work together form a body structure called a tissue. There are four main kinds of tissue. Epithelial tissue forms the skin. Muscle tissue forms muscles. Nervous tissue forms brain, spinal cord and nerve. Connective tissue provides packing and support for other tissues. Tissues that work together form an organ.

Internal organs

Front and back views of a human body locate most main organs, except sex organs, in the neck, thorax (chest), and abdomen (belly).

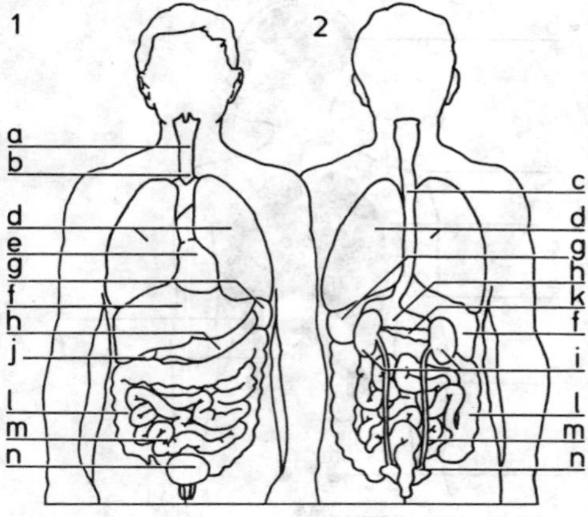

1 Front view
2 Back view
a Larynx
b Trachea
c Oesophagus
d Lungs
e Heart
f Liver
g Spleen
h Stomach
i Kidneys
j Gall bladder
k Pancreas
l Large intestine
m Small intestine
n Bladder

Weights of organs

Organs performing different tasks have different weights. Here are weights of 10 organs. Letters indicate locations in the diagram.

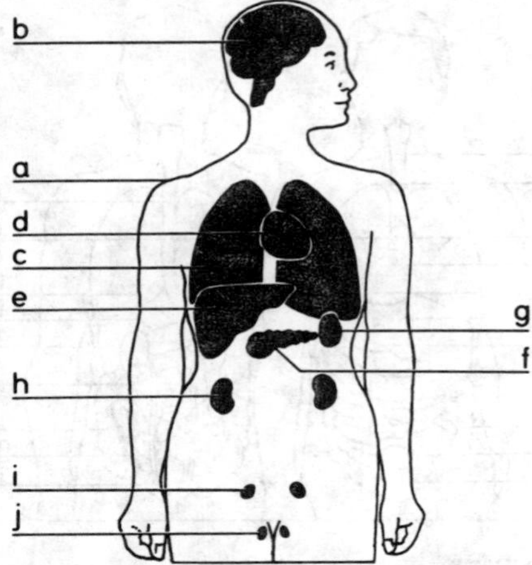

a Skin 3250g (7.16lb)
b Brain 1400g (3.08lb)
c Lungs (each) 600g (1.3lb)
d Heart 280g (10oz)
e Liver 1420g (3.1lb)
f Pancreas 85g (3oz)
g Spleen 200g (7oz)
h Kidneys (each) 140g (5oz)
i Ovaries (each) 3g (0.1oz)
j Testicles (each) 12g (0.4oz)

Sizes and shapes of organs
Eight kinds of organs appear here on the same scale. The hand gives an idea of sizes. Lungs and skin are too big to be shown this way. Laid flat, a human skin would occupy as much space as a single bed.

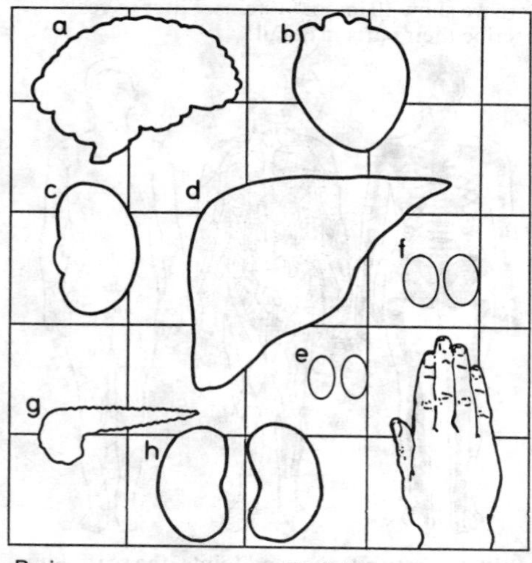

a Brain
b Heart
c Spleen
d Liver
e Testicles
f Ovaries
g Pancreas
h Kidneys

Major systems

Body tissues are largely grouped in organs arranged to form systems performing different major tasks. (Some organs play a part in more than one system.) Here we show 10 major systems. Later pages describe their parts in detail.

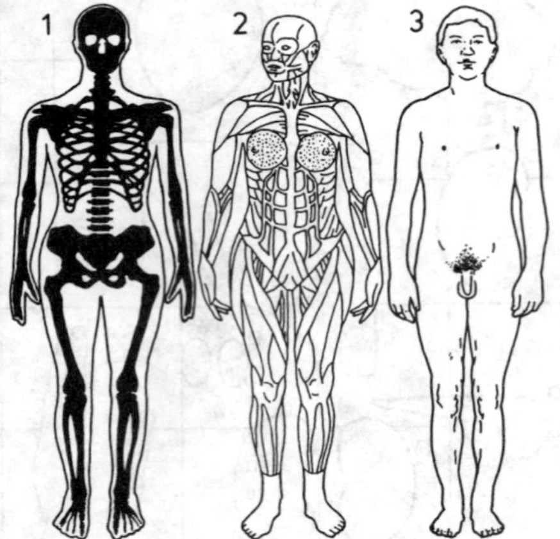

1 Skeletal system Bones and joints, the scaffolding or framework of the body. Pages 46–55.
2 Muscular system Muscles, elastic fibres that move limbs and drive blood around the body. Pages 56–59.

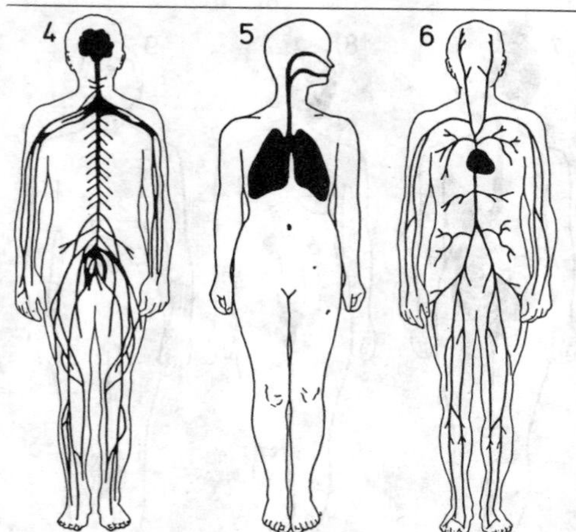

3 Skin, nails and hair The skin, a barrier that protects the body and helps control its temperature. Pages 60–63.

4 Nervous system Brain, spinal cord and nerves, the body's control centre and communication system. including the five senses. Pages 64–79.

5 Respiratory system The breathing organs: nose, windpipe, lungs, etc., which take in oxygen and remove carbon dioxide waste. Pages 80–83.

6 Circulatory system Blood vessels, heart, and lymphatic system; supplying cells, removing wastes, and helping fight disease. Pages 84–94.

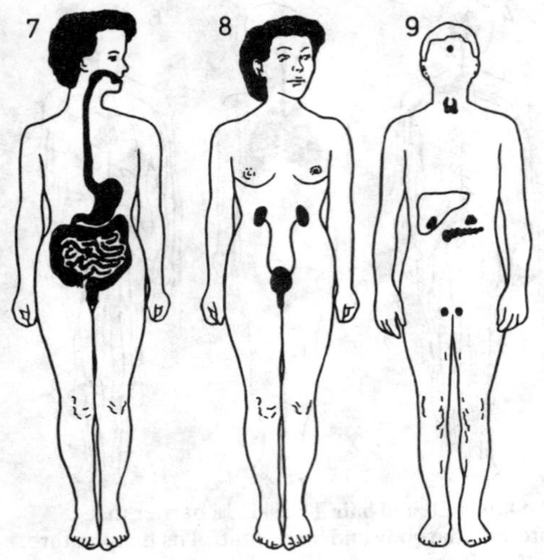

7 Digestive system Mouth, alimentary canal, and glands, including the liver, that break down food for use inside the body. Pages 95–107.
8 Urinary system Kidneys, bladder, and tubes that remove body waste as urine. Pages 108–110.
9 Endocrine system Glands producing hormones that regulate a number of body functions. Pages 111–117.

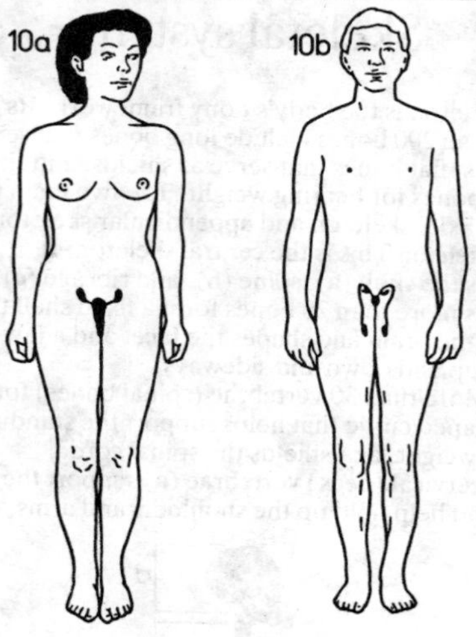

10a Female reproductive system Organs for producing eggs and babies. Pages 119–121
10b Male reproductive system Organs for producing and releasing sperm. Page 118.

Skeletal system

The skeleton is the body's bony framework. Its more than 200 bones include long bones that serve as levers, flat bones that serve as shields, and short, strong bones for bearing weight. The two main parts are the axial skeleton and appendicular skeleton.

Axial skeleton This is the central skeleton. It includes the skull (**a**), spine (**b**), and ribcage (**c**).

Skull Its more than 20 bones form a fixed shell that shields the brain and shapes the face, and a jaw that moves up and down and sideways.

Spine More than 30 vertebrae (spinal bones) form an S-shaped curve that helps support the standing body's weight, and shields the spinal cord.

Seven cervical (neck) vertebrae (**a**) support the head and help hold up the shoulders and arms.

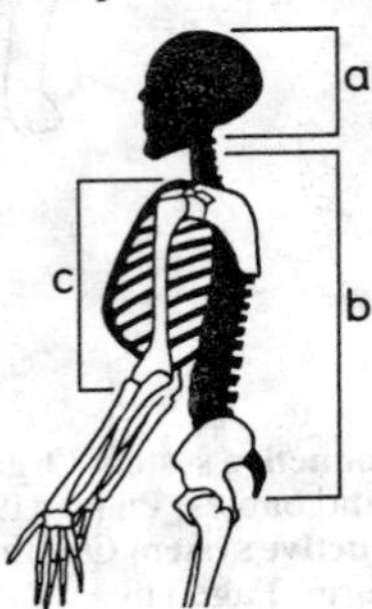

Twelve thoracic vertebrae (**b**) support the upper back. Twelve pairs of ribs (**c**) curve forward from these vertebrae to join the sternum (breastbone) (**d**). Ribs and breastbone protect the lungs and heart and help to work the lungs.
Five lumbar vertebrae (**e**) support the lower back.
Five fused vertebrae (**f**) form the sacrum. This joins bones and supports all weight above.
Five fused vertebrae form the coccyx (**g**), the tiny vestige of a tail.

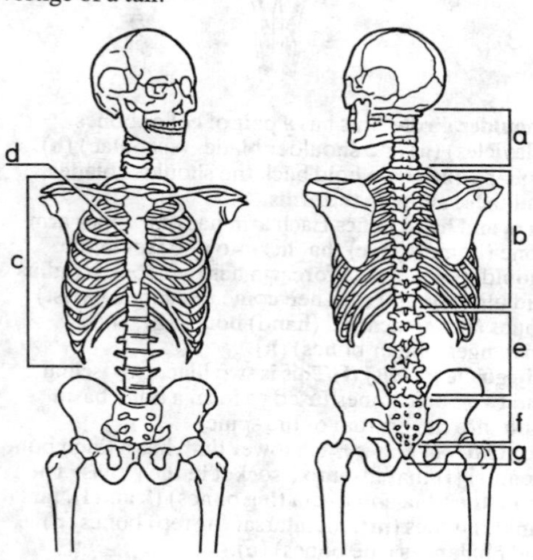

Appendicular skeleton
The appendicular skeleton contains arm and leg bones and the bones supporting these.

Shoulder girdle This hás a pair of collar bones (clavicles) (**a**) and shoulder blades (scapulae) (**b**). Collar bones help hold back the shoulder blades, and these support the arms.
Arm and hand bones Each arm has one upper arm bone (humerus) (**c**) that fits into a socket in the shoulder blade. The forearm has two bones (radius and ulna) (**d** and **e**). Then come the carpal (wrist) bones (**f**), metacarpal (hand) bones (**g**), and phalanges (finger bones) (**h**).
Hip girdle (pelvis) (**i**) This is two iliac, two ischial, and two pubic bones fused to form a bony basin built into the bottom of the spine.
Leg and foot bones Each lower limb has a thigh bone (femur) (**j**) that fits into a socket in the pelvis. Then come the tibia and fibula (leg bones) (**k** and **l**), tarsal (ankle) bones (**m**), metatarsal (instep) bones (**n**), and phalanges (toe bones) (**o**).

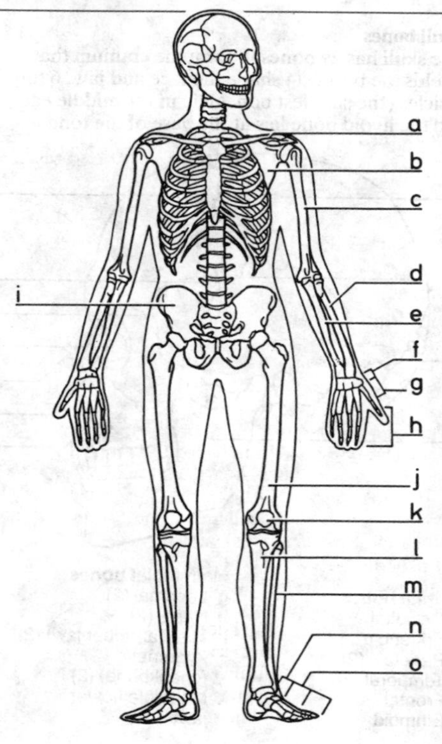
a
b
c
d
e
f
g
h
i
j
k
l
m
n
o

Skull bones

The skull has 29 bones: 8 form the cranium that shields the brain, 14 shape the face and jaw; 6 tiny ossicles (the smallest bones) lie in the middle ear and the hyoid bone lies at the base of the tongue.

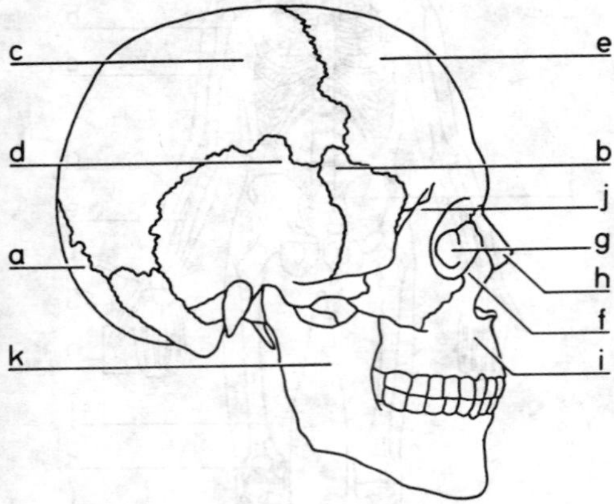

Cranial bones

- **a** Occipital
- **b** Sphenoid
- **c** Parietals (2)
- **d** Temporal (2)
- **e** Frontal
- **f** Ethmoid

Main facial bones

- **g** Lacrimal (2)
- **h** Nasal (2)
- **i** Maxilla (upper jaw) (2)
- **j** Zygomatic (cheekbone) (2)
- **k** Mandible (lower jawbone)

Bones of the feet
The 26 foot bones support the body and serve as levers to lift and move it forward when you walk or run. More than 100 ligaments hold the foot's 33 joints in place. Lengthwise and crosswise arches give the foot its springiness.

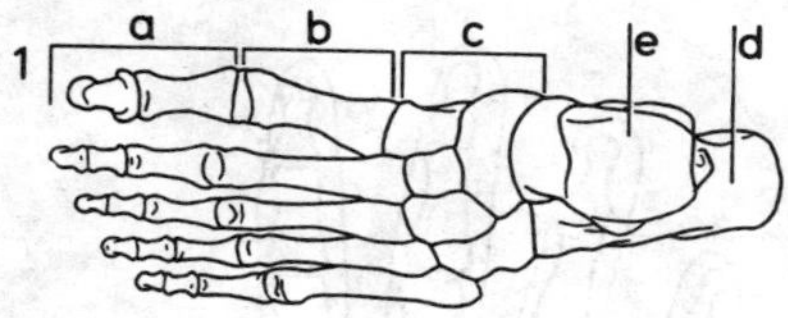

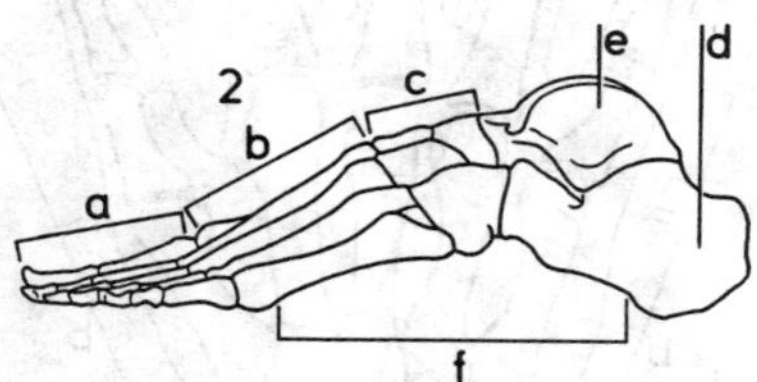

1 Top view of foot
2 Side view of foot
a Phalanges (toe bones) (14)
b Metatarsals (instep bones) (5)
c Tarsals (ankle bones) (7)
d Calcaneus (heel bone)
e Talus (hinged with leg bones)
f Lengthwise arch

Bones of the hands
Twenty-seven bones form the framework of the hand. Thumb bones that can be pressed against finger bones make hands capable of grasping objects. Thirty-five muscles control the precise movements of each hand.

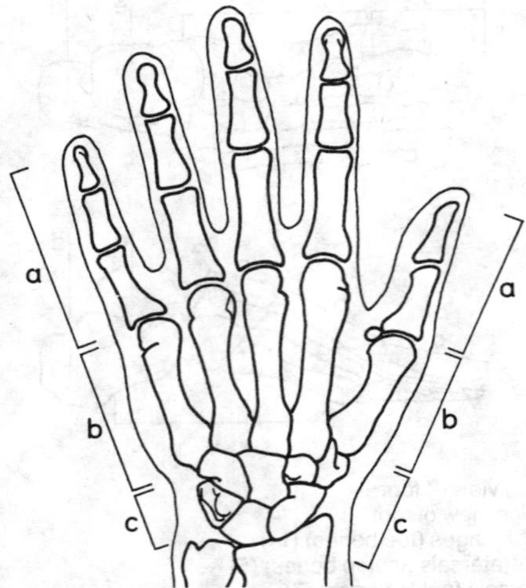

a Phalanges (thumb and finger bones) (14)
b Metacarpals (bones of the palm of the hand) (5)
c Carpal bones (wrist bones) (8)

Bone and cartilage
Bone is the hard, strong substance that the skeleton is made of. Bone forms during growth as minerals bit by bit replace cartilage. Cartilage is the white springy substance also known as gristle.
Bone structure Bone is mainly calcium and phosphorus, but one-third is living matter. This is chiefly the fibrous protein collagen. Bone has two types of tissue. In a long bone, hard, dense compact tissue (**a**) forms the outside. A light, spongy honeycomb of cancellous tissue (**b**) is in each bulging end. Ends also hold red marrow and there is yellow marrow in the medullary cavity (**c**) between.

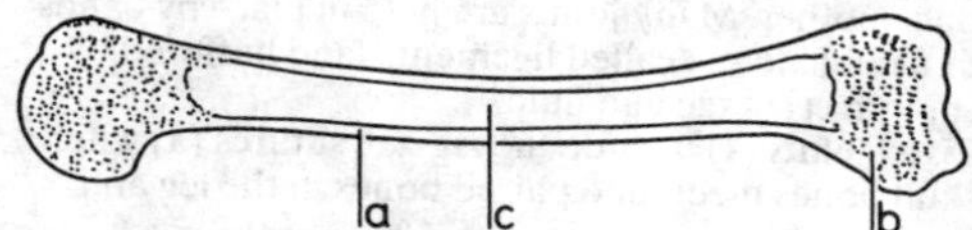

How bone is made Bones are not dry, dead material; one third of them is living tissue with a constant turnover of cells carrying out the jobs of maintenance and repair. Bones are serviced by blood vessels, nerves and lymph vessels (transporting body fluids) which run through a labyrinth of tiny canals. Special cells (osteoblasts) can carry out repair work on bones while others (osteoclasts) can dissolve and break down damaged bones so that they can be repaired.
What bone does Bone forms an inner framework for the body. It stores calcium, phosphorus, fat and other substances. Bone also manufactures blood

cells, and helps remove some harmful substances from blood.

Cartilage structure Cartilage is formed of the hard protein collagen and the elastic protein elastin.

What cartilage does Cartilage forms the skeleton in unborn babies. In an adult, cartilage gives shape to the nose and outer ears, keeps large airways open, links ribs, and buffers joints.

Joints

Joints are where two or more bones meet. A joint can be fixed or movable. Fixed joints help to protect abutting bones from damage caused by blows. Movable joints let bones move smoothly against one another. Many joints are held in place by bands of flexible tissue called ligaments, and buffered by smooth cartilage and fluid.

Fixed joints (**1**) include the zig-zag sutures (**a**) where skull bones meet, and paired bones in the leg and forearm (**b**).

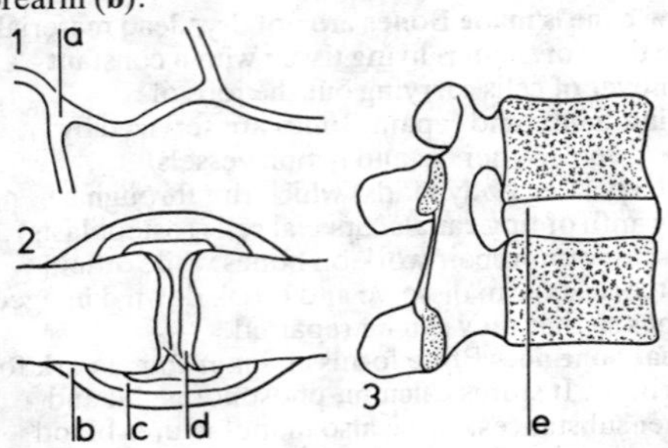

Synovial joints (2) are movable joints like those of shoulder, hip, and knee. Ligaments form a fibrous joint capsule (**b**) lined with a lubricating fatty synovial membrane (**c**) and enclosing two bones' ends capped by smooth articular cartilage (**d**).
Cartilaginous joints (3) include those between the spinal bones, allowing slight movement only. A fibrocartilage cushion (**e**) provides a buffer between each bone and its neighbour.

Joint movements

Some movable joints allow freer movement than others. The main kinds of movable joint are pivot, hinge, and ball-and-socket joints.
Pivot joints (1) permit a turning movement. A pivot joint where the skull rests on the spine lets you turn your head. Another in the elbow lets you turn your hand palm upward.
Hinge joints (2) permit to and fro movements like those of a door hinge. Elbow, knee, and finger joints allow this kind of movement.
Ball-and-socket joints (3) are where the round end of one bone sits in a hollow in another bone. Ball-and-socket joints allow the freest movements of all. The ball-and-socket joints of hips and shoulders let you swing your legs and arms inwards, outwards, forwards, or backwards.

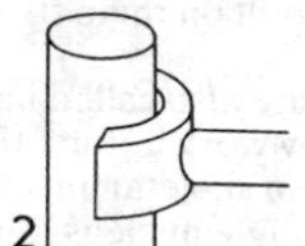

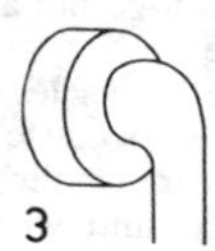

Muscular system

Muscles are tough elastic tissues made of cells called muscle fibres. The body's more than 600 muscles account for 40 per cent of its weight. Muscles work limbs, lungs, and other parts of the body and largely give it bulk and shape. They come in three main types: skeletal, smooth, and cardiac.

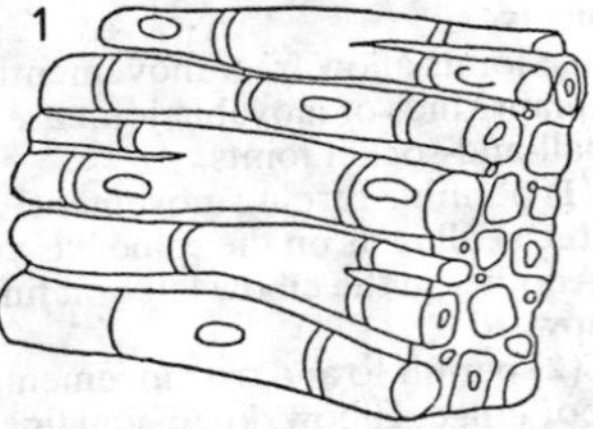

Skeletal muscles (1) are also called voluntary or striated (striped) muscles. These have many large, long, cylinder-shaped, cross-banded fibres each with many nuclei. The muscle ends are mostly joined to bones by tendons of tough, flexible, connective tissue. Skeletal muscles form much of the legs, arms, chest, neck, and face. They hold bones together and pull on them to make them move.

Smooth muscles (2) are also called involuntary muscles because they work automatically. Their fibres are smaller than skeletal muscles', not striped, and with a single nucleus. Smooth muscles

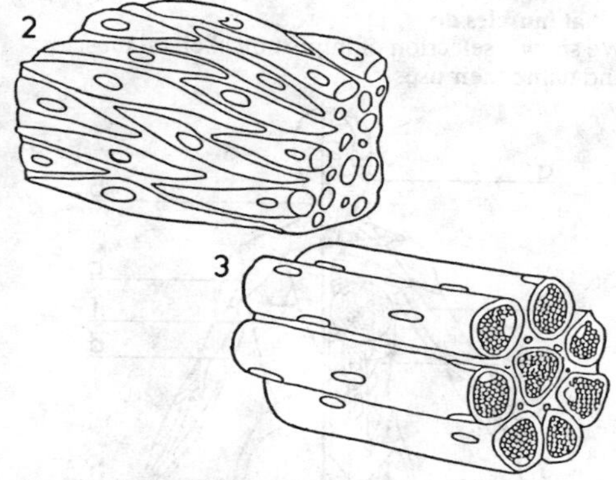

occur in the intestines, stomach, blood vessels, and bladder. These muscles rhythmically contract, moving food, blood, and urine through the body. **Cardiac muscle (3)** forms the walls of the heart. Cardiac muscle is striped like skeletal muscle but works automatically and has only one nucleus per fibre, like smooth muscle.

Fuel for muscles

Muscles obtain their energy from glucose in the blood. Glucose combines with oxygen, releasing energy. Muscular activity also produces heat and lactic acid, water, and carbon dioxide wastes removed by blood. Vigorous exercise steps up the muscles' needs for oxygen and blood, producing panting and a rapid heart rate.

What muscles do
We show a selection of important skeletal muscles and name their uses.

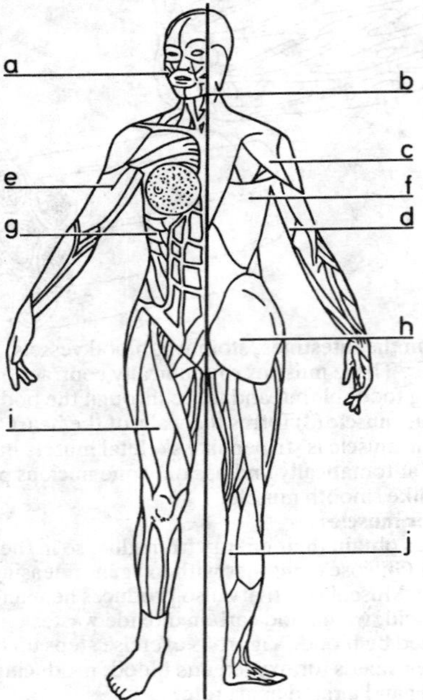

a Masseter (chews)
b Trapezius (holds head back)
c Deltoid (lifts arm)
d Triceps (straightens arm)
e Biceps (bends arm)
f Latissimus dorsi (strengthens back)
g Intercostals (move ribs)
h Gluteus maximus (used in standing up)
i Rectus femoris (straightens leg)
j Gastrocnemius (used in walking)

How muscles work
Muscles pull but cannot push. So to and fro movements need muscles that work in pairs with opposite effects. Bending and straightening the arm involves biceps (**a**) and triceps (**b**) muscles.

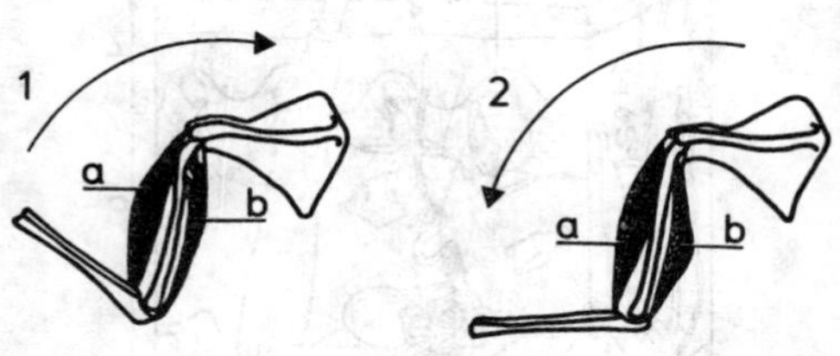

1 When the biceps contracts the triceps relaxes and the arm bends.
2 When the triceps contracts the biceps relaxes and the arm straightens.

Skin, nails and hair

Skin is the largest body organ, peeled off, an average man's skin occupies about 1.9 sq m (20 sq ft).

Structure Skin has an outer layer, the epidermis, an inner layer, the dermis, and subcutaneous tissue.

Epidermis (A) The base of the epidermis produces new cells and the brown pigment melanin. The amount of melanin helps to determine skin and hair

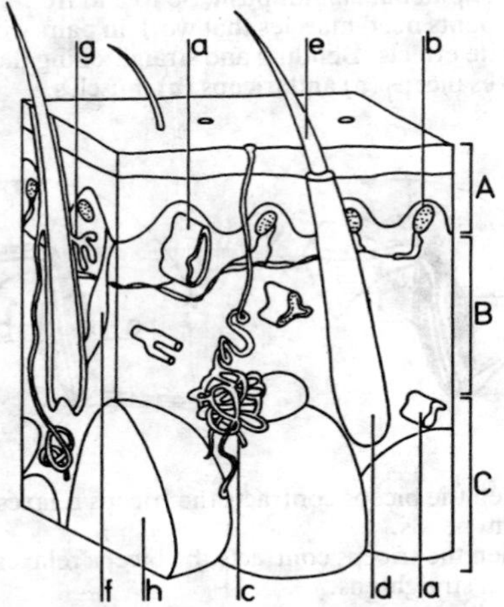

colour. The epidermis surface contains old dying cells of the horny protein keratin. This also forms the hair and nail. Nails are outgrowths of the epidermis.

Dermis (B) The dermis contains elastic fibres that give skin tensile strength. The dermis also has blood vessels (**a**), nerve endings (**b**), sweat glands (**c**), and hair follicles (**d**): baglike structures from which grow the hair shafts (**e**). Each hair has an erector muscle (**f**) and a sebaceous gland (**g**) releasing oily sebum that helps keep skin supple.

Subcutaneous tissue (**C**) Below the dermis lies the subcutaneous tissue, mainly connective tissue, fat (**h**), and blood vessels.

What it does Skin provides a flexible, waterproof barrier that keeps in body fluids and keeps out bacteria and harmful rays from the Sun. Nerve endings in skin sense heat, cold, pain, and pressure. Sweat glands and tiny blood vessels in skin help to control body temperature. Subcutaneous tissue buffers the body's internal structures against blows.

Nail formation

Nails form before birth. Certain epidermal cells in toes and fingers divide (**a**) and the upper cells accumulate hard keratin which produces a nail plate (**b**). This plate grows out of the nail groove (**c**) and over the skin, forming a fingernail or toenail.

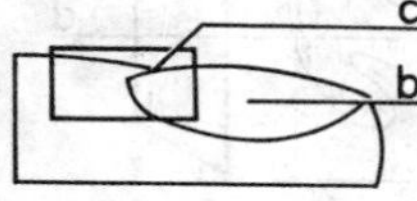

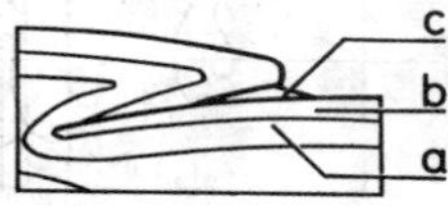

Hair formation
Hair forms before birth. First, part of the epidermis grows thicker (**a**). Then it invades the dermis (**b**) and forms a projection called a papilla (**c**). Its multiplying cells produce a hair (**d**) which accumulates the hard protein keratin as it grows up and away from its supply of nourishment. Other cells in the papilla form a keratinized root sheath (**e**) which produces a sebaceous gland (**f**).

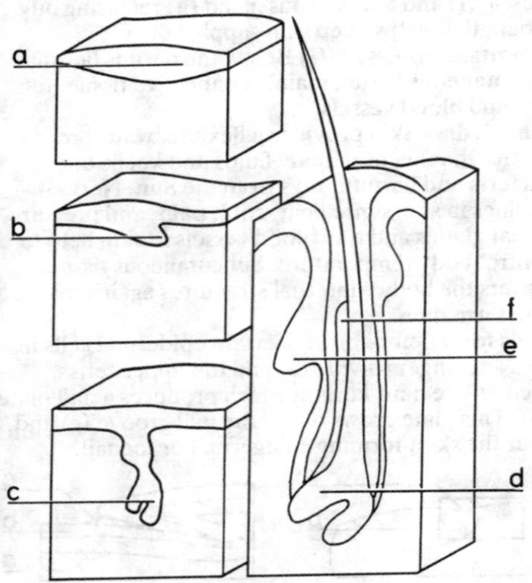

Skin and temperature control
In hot weather skin helps cool down the overheating body (**1**). Sweat glands (**a**) release sweat that cools the skin. Blood capillaries dilate (**b**), and radiate heat through the skin.
In cold weather skin helps stop the body losing heat (**2**). Sweat glands (**a**) close up. Blood capillaries constrict (**b**), and hairs grow erect (**c**), trapping a thick layer of still air that insulates the skin.

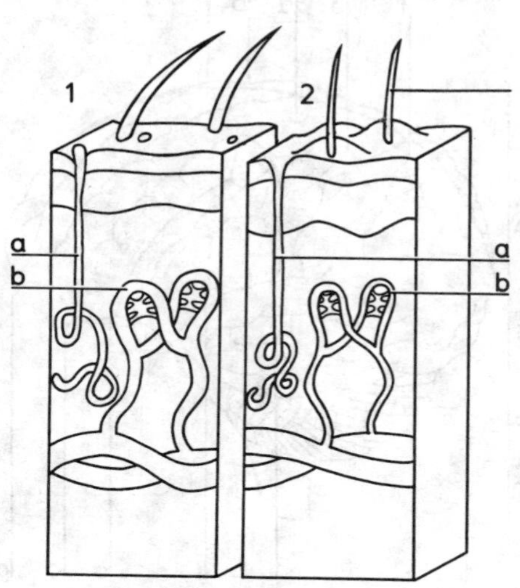

Nervous system

The brain and spinal cord comprise the central nervous system. The brain's billions of nerve cells (neurons) control consciousness, emotions, thought, movement, and unconscious body functions.

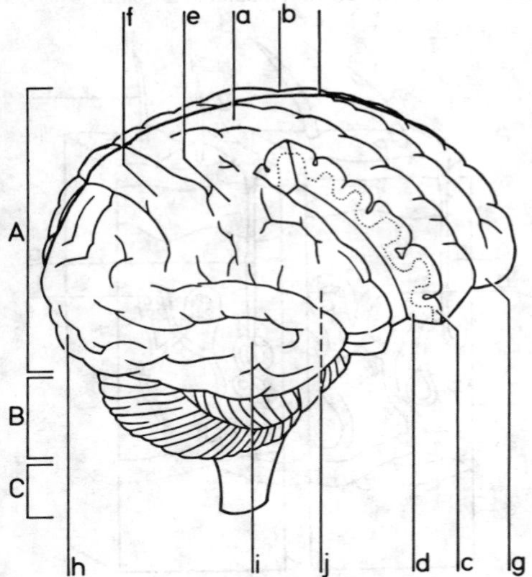

Brain structure
The brain looks like a giant wrinkled walnut crammed inside the skull.
Cerebrospinal fluid and meninges (layered membranes) cushion it against damage. Its main parts are the cerebrum (**A**), cerebellum (**B**), and brainstem (**C**).
The cerebrum takes up about seven-tenths of the nervous system. It comprises a right cerebral hemisphere (**a**) and left cerebral hemisphere (**b**) connected deep down by a mass of linking fibres. The cerebrum's deeply wrinkled cortex (surface layer) contains grey matter (nerve cells) (**c**) overlying white matter (nerve trunks) (**d**). Certain cerebral areas deal with special functions: motor cortex (**e**), voluntary movement; sensory cortex (**f**), bodily sensations; frontal lobe (**g**), personality; occipital lobe (**h**), sight; hearing centre (**i**), hearing; and speech centre (**j**). Below the mass of fibres linking cerebral hemispheres lie the hypothalamus and other control, co-ordination, and relay centres, some controlling emotion and behaviour.
The cerebellum is the second largest region of the brain, projecting below the back of the cerebrum. This structure deals with balance and co-ordinating complex movements of the body.
The brainstem is a stalk of nerve fibres and nuclei that joins the spinal cord to the cerebellum and cerebrum. Brainstem centres automatically control activities like breathing, heartbeat, and digestion.

Neurons
Neurons are nerve cells, and neuron networks form the nervous system. Sensory neurons send signals from nerve endings in eye, ear, skin, etc., to the brain. Motor neurons send signals from brain and spinal cord to muscles. Interneurons provide intervening links.

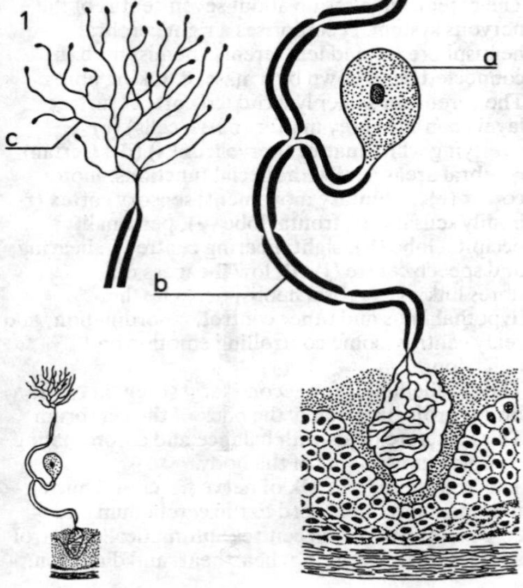

A sensory neuron (**1**) and motor neuron (**2**) each have three main parts: a rounded cell body (**a**), long, narrow, insulated axon (**b**), and branching dendrites (**c**). Electrical impulses flow through the axon and dendrites and chemical messengers jump the gap (synapse) between one neuron and another.

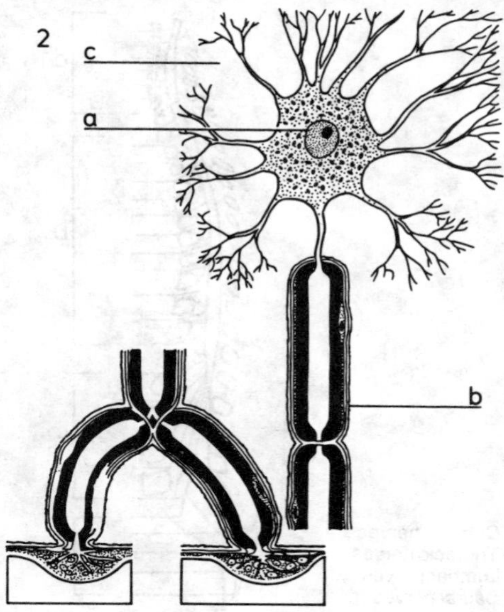

Spinal cord

This soft, curved cylinder of nerve fibres about 46cm (18in) long (**1**) runs from the brain down through the vertebrae. From the spinal cord 31 pairs of nerves branch out into the body. These spinal nerves plus 12 pairs of cranial nerves rooted in the

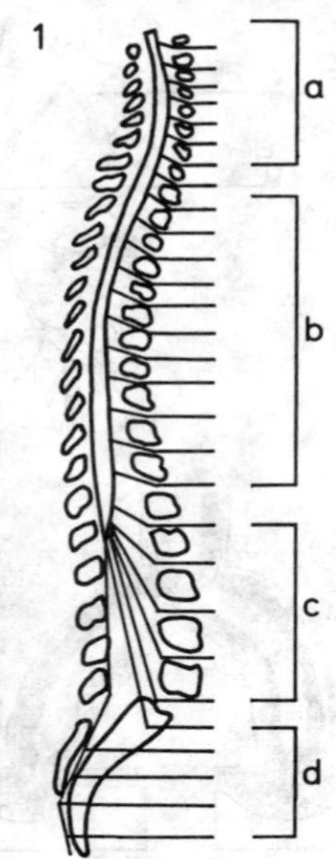

a Cervical nerves
b Thoracic nerves
c Lumbar nerves
d Sacral nerves

brain form the so-called peripheral nervous system.
Structure This section (**2**) shows a piece of spinal cord (**a**) passing through the vertebrae (**b**). Meninges (**c, d**) protect the cord. Spinal nerves (**d**) leave the cord at intervals between vertebrae. Spinal nerves receive sensory impulses from and take motor signals to specific regions of the body.

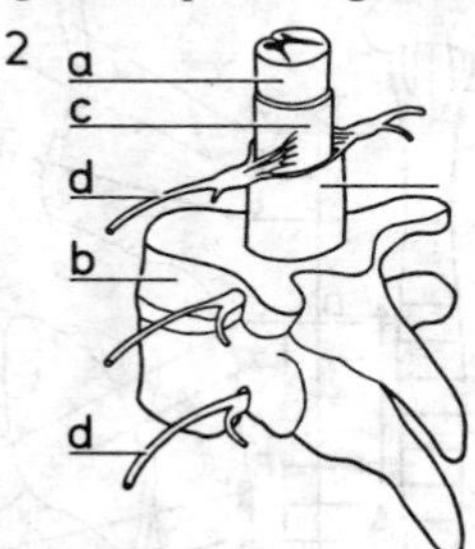

Peripheral nervous system
The peripheral nerves form the somatic and autonomic nervous systems. The somatic system involves sensory nerves sending signals from sense organs to the central nervous system, and motor nerves sending signals from the central nervous system to muscles under voluntary control. The autonomic nervous system comprises the sympathetic and parasympathetic systems, producing actions that balance one another. Probably directed by the hypothalamus in the brain, they handle activities outside conscious control.

The sympathetic nervous system (1) sends blood to brain, heart, lungs, etc., preparing us for bodily exertion. Nerves from the spinal cord's thoracic (**A**) and lumbar (**B**) regions pass through nerve knots (ganglia) (**C–G**) to act on different organs:

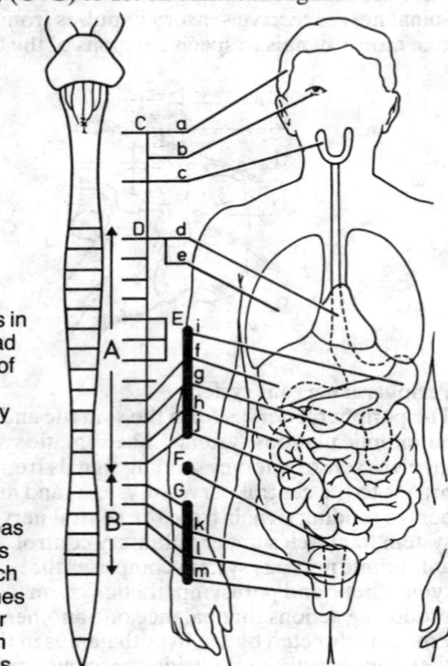

a Blood vessels in the head
b Pupils of eyes
c Salivary glands
d Heart
e Lungs
f Liver
g Pancreas
h Kidneys
i Stomach
j Intestines
k Bladder
l Rectum
m Genitals

The parasympathetic nervous system (2) dominates the sympathetic nervous system when we are at rest. It reduces much of the activity that system triggers, reducing heart rate but sending blood to the intestines, and increasing output of digestive juices. Nerves from the brainstem (**A**) and spinal cord's sacral region (**B**) act on different organs:

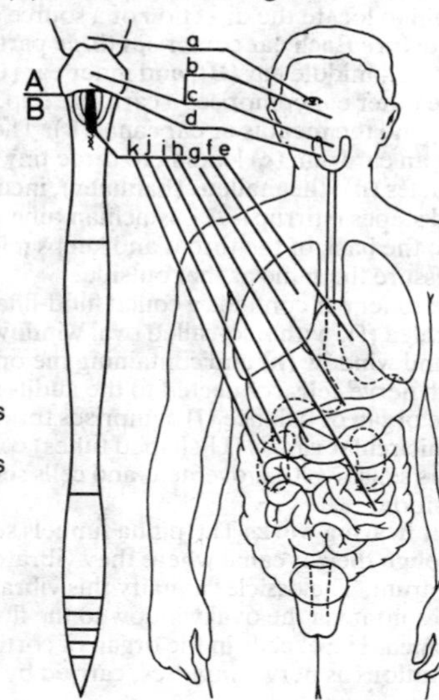

- **a** Pupils of eyes
- **b** Nasal membranes
- **c** Palate membranes
- **d** Salivary glands
- **e** Heart
- **f** Lungs
- **g** Stomach
- **h** Intestines
- **i** Pancreas
- **j** Liver
- **k** Kidneys

Ears
Ears contain structures that enable us to hear and keep our balance. The human ear is sensitive to sounds ranging in loudness from 10 to 140 decibels (10 million million times as loud as 10), and ranging in pitch from 20 to a high 20,000 hertz cycles per second. The distance between both ears helps the brain to locate the direction of a source of sound.
Structure Each ear comprises three parts: the outer ear (**A**), middle ear (**B**), and inner ear (**C**).
The outer ear comprises a cartilage flap, the pinna (**a**), and the meatus or ear canal (**b**). The middle ear has an eardrum (**c**) leading to three tiny bones or ossicles (**d**): the malleus (hammer), incus (anvil), and stapes (stirrup). A eustachian tube (**e**) opens into the back of the throat and keeps middle ear air pressure the same as that outside.
The inner ear contains a coiled fluid-filled tube, the cochlea (**f**), with a so-called oval window (**g**) and round window (**h**) and containing the organ of Corti with nerve cells connected to the auditory nerve (**i**). The organ of balance (**j**) comprises three fluid-filled semicircular canals (U-shaped tubes) containing hairs sensitive to movement and cells sensing bodily position.
How hearing works The pinna funnels sound waves through the ear canal where they vibrate the eardrum. The ossicles amplify this vibration and transmit it via the oval window to the fluid in the cochlea. Here, cells in the organ of corti interpret vibrations as nerve impulses, carried by the auditory

nerve to the brain. Meanwhile vibrations leave the cochlea through the round window.

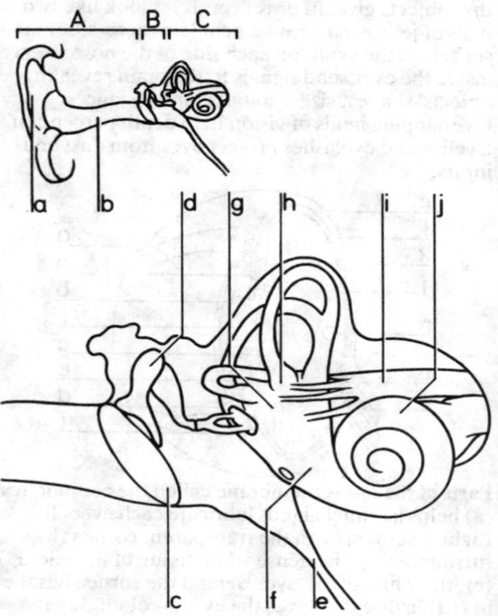

Eyes

Eyes see the world around us by sensing the light that objects give off or reflect. Eyes look like two balls of jelly each about 2.5cm (1in) across, set in sockets in the skull, on each side of the nose. Nerves inside the eyes send signals to the brain revealing objects' shapes, sizes, colours, and distances. Overlapping fields of vision help depth perception. Eyelids and eyelashes protect eyes from dust and injury.

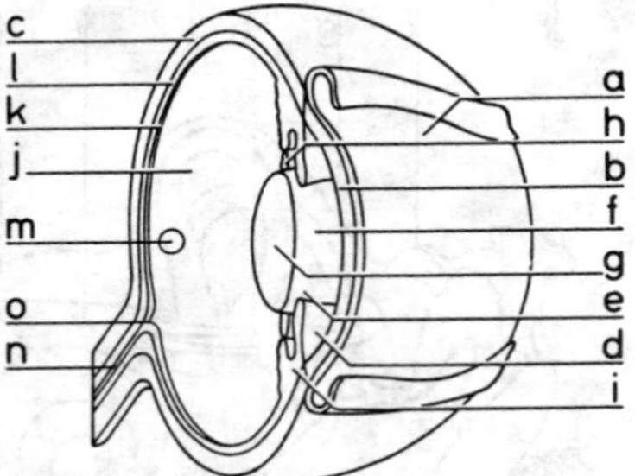

Parts of the eye A membrane called the conjunctiva (**a**) helps lacrimal glands lubricate each eyeball. Light enters through the transparent cornea (**b**), surrounded by the dense white tissue of the sclera (**c**), the white of the eye. Behind the cornea lies the iris (**d**), a disc that gives the eye its colour. Light enters through the pupil (**e**), the round black hole in the middle of the iris. Here light passes through the watery fluid (aqueous humour) in the anterior chamber (**f**), and through the transparent lens (**g**), attached by suspensory ligaments (**h**) to the ciliary body (**i**). Its muscles alter lens shape to focus light rays from objects near and far away. Light continues through the jelly-like vitreous body (**j**) to the light-sensitive retina (**k**) and the dark choroid layer (**l**), which absorbs excess light.

In the retina rod cells sense dim light, cone cells sense bright light and colours. Cone cells alone line the fovea (**m**), a depression where vision is sharpest. Light sensed by the retina triggers impulses that pass through the optic nerve (**n**) to the back of the brain. The nerve's point of entry in the eyeball forms a blind spot (**o**) in our vision.

Eyeball movement

Six ocular muscles attached to the outside of the sclera move the eyeball in different ways:

1 Up and down. Superior rectus (**a**) and inferior rectus (**b**) muscles.

2 Left and right. Lateral rectus (**c**) and medial rectus (**d**) muscles.

3 Downwards and outwards and upwards and outwards. Superior oblique (**e**) and inferior oblique (**f**) muscles.

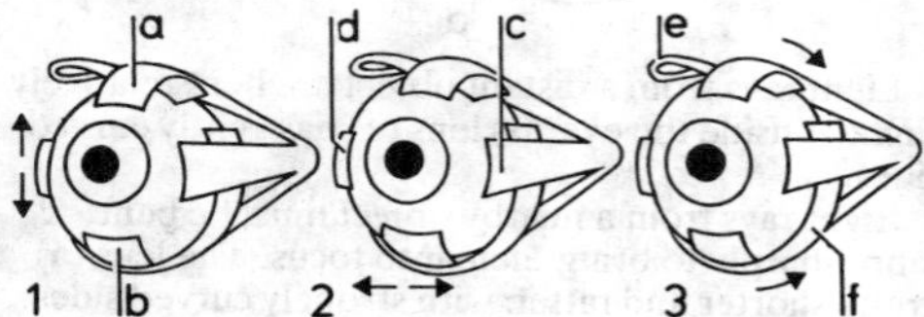

How eyes focus
Inside the eye, light rays from an object are bent by cornea, lens, aqueous humour, and vitreous body, so that the rays come to a focus on the retina. (The focused image is upside down, but the brain 'sees' it the right way up).

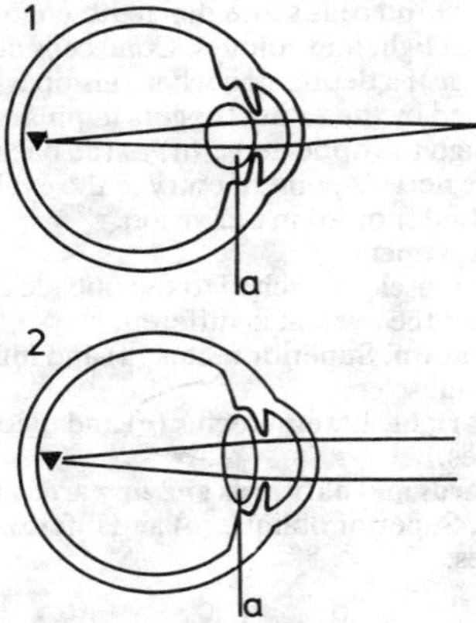

1 Light rays from a distant object are bent relatively slightly inside the eye. Its lens (**a**) has gently curved sides.
2 Light rays from a nearby object must be bent more sharply to bring them into focus. The lens (**a**) grows shorter and fatter, with strongly curved sides.

Sense of smell

Our sense of smell is less keen than a dog's, yet some people can identify 10,000 odours, all evidently based on combinations of just seven. We smell substances whose molecules are breathed into the roof of each nasal cavity (**a**) and dissolved on a patch of olfactory membrane (**b**) armed with 100 million smell receptor cells equipped with tiny sensitive 'hairs'. Scent molecules react with these to stimulate nerve impulses in the receptor cells. Olfactory nerves transmit these signals to olfactory bulbs (**c**) then via olfactory tracts (**d**) to the smell centre (**e**) in the limbic system deep in the brain.

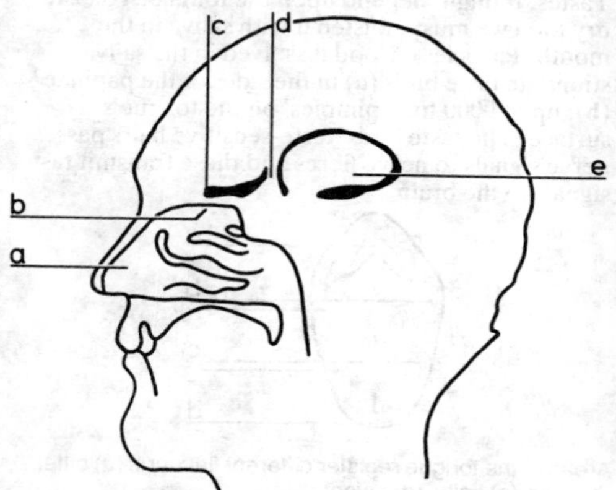

Sense of taste

Taste is closely geared to smell. Foods' flavours are partly smells detected by the olfactory membrane in the nasal cavity.

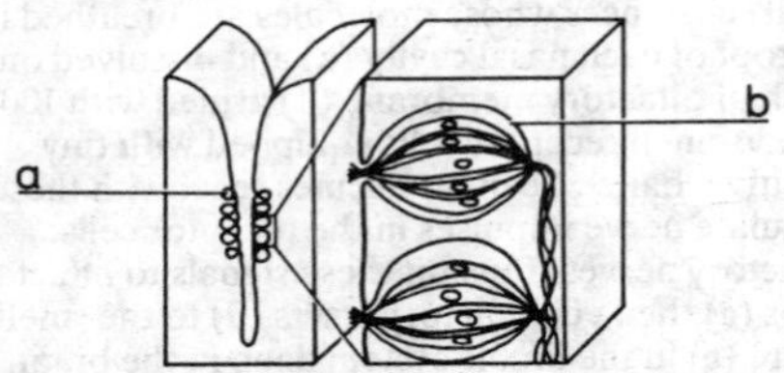

Tastes, though, depend upon the tongue. To taste dry food we must moisten it with saliva in the mouth. Particles of food dissolved in the saliva stimulate taste buds (**a**) in the sides of the papillae (**b**): up to 9000 tiny 'pimples' on the tongue's surface. The taste buds' taste-sensitive hairs pass nerve signals to nerve fibres and these transmit taste signals to the brain.

Areas of the tongue register different flavours: (**a**) bitter, (**b**) sour, (**c**) salty, (**d**) sweet.

Skin sensitivity

Specialized nerve endings in the skin send signals that the brain identifies as touch, pain, pressure, heat, and cold.

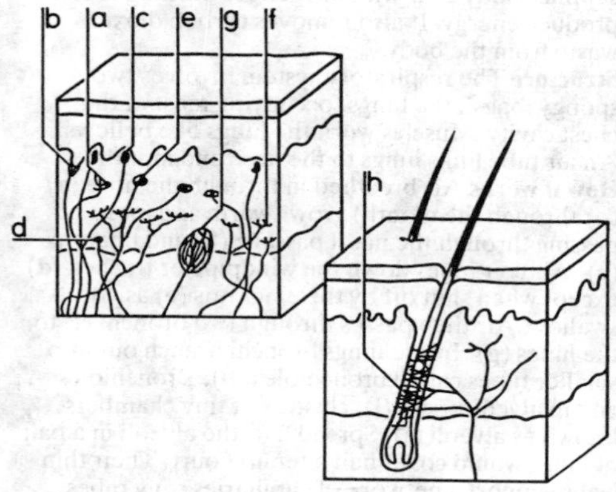

a Free nerve endings (pain)
b Merkel's discs (touch)
c Meissner's corpuscles (touch)
d Beaded nerve net (pain)
e Krause's end bulbs (cold)
f Ruffini corpuscles (heat)
g Pacinian corpuscles (pressure, stretching, and vibration)
h Hair organs (touch)

Respiratory system

This lets air in and out of the body. The system supplies body cells with oxygen for burning food to produce energy. It also removes carbon dioxide waste from the body.

Structure The respiratory system involves two spongy 'bags', the lungs, occupying most of the chest cavity. Muscles work the lungs like bellows. An air tube links lungs to the nose and mouth.

How it works Air breathed in through the nose (**a**) (or through the mouth) grows warm and moist on passing through the nasal passage (**b**) and pharynx (**c**). Air continues down the windpipe or trachea (**d**) except when shut off by the epiglottis (**e**) as you swallow. Air then passes through two bronchi (**f**) to the lungs (**g**). Inside lungs bronchi branch out into smaller tubes called bronchioles (**h**). Bronchioles end in alveolar sacs (**i**), clusters of tiny chambers known as alveoli (**j**). Spread flat, the alveoli in a pair of lungs would cover half a tennis court. Their thin walls support a network of capillaries, tiny tubes containing blood. Gases pass through alveolar walls between the lungs and blood supply.

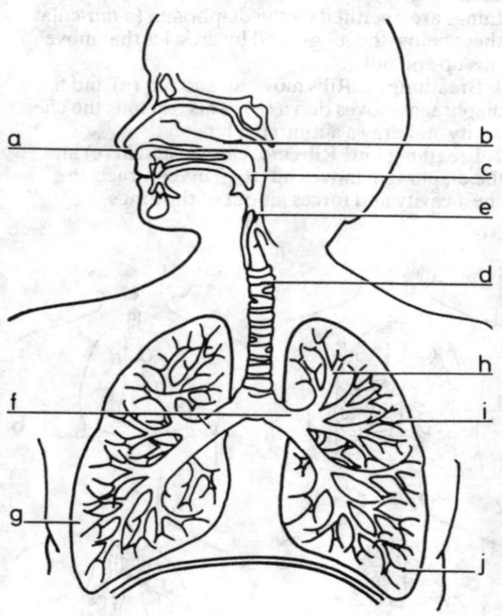
a
b
c
e
d
h
f
i
g
j

Breathing
Lungs are operated by the diaphragm (a muscular sheet below the lungs) and by muscles that move ribs up and out.
1 Breathing in: Ribs move up and out (**a**) and the diaphragm moves down (**b**). This expands the chest cavity and draws air into the lungs.
2 Breathing out: Ribs move down and in (**c**) and the diaphragm moves up (**d**). This contracts the chest cavity and forces air out of the lungs.

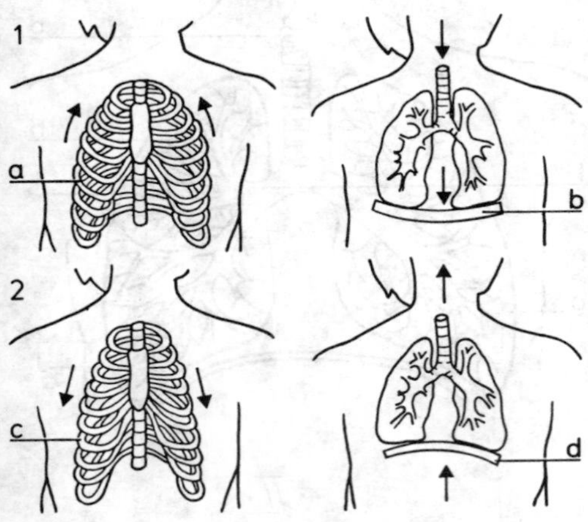

Voice
Vocal sounds depend on special structures in the body's airways.

How the voice works Breathed-out air flows through the larynx or voice-box (**a**), a broad part of the upper windpipe protected by tough cartilage that forms the Adam's apple (**b**). Two bands of tissue called vocal cords (**c**) form a V-shaped opening across the larynx. When we speak, these tauten, narrowing the opening. Breathed-out air vibrates the cords, producing sounds: the longer the cords, the higher the pitch. Sounds vary with positions of tongue (**d**), lips (**e**), and teeth (**f**). The nasal cavity (**g**) gives resonance.

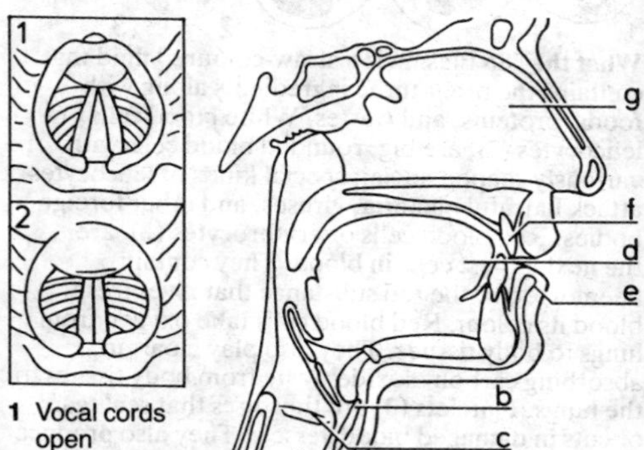

1 Vocal cords open
2 Vocal cords closed

Circulatory system

Blood
Blood is a complex red fluid that brings all body tissues the food and oxygen they need to grow and stay alive. It also helps remove waste products. Some substances in blood help fight disease.
Substances in blood The four main ingredients of blood are plasma, red blood cells, white blood cells, and platelets.

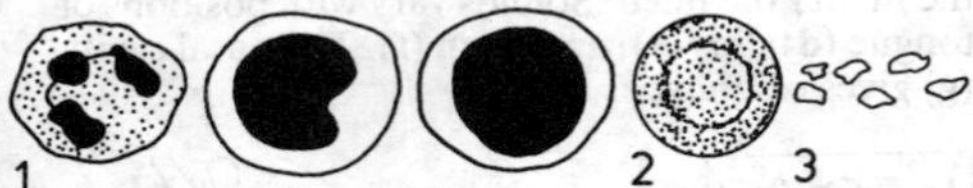

What they do Plasma is a straw-coloured fluid that contains the other three ingredients along with foods, proteins, and wastes. White blood cells or leucocytes (**1**), are big, rounded blood cells with variously shaped nuclei; special kinds of leucocytes attack harmful bacteria, viruses, and other foreign bodies. Red blood cells or erythrocytes (**2**), are the next largest cells in blood. They contain haemoglobin, the red substance that gives fresh blood its colour. Red blood cells take oxygen from lungs to body tissues. They also play a part in absorbing carbon dioxide waste from body tissues to the lungs. Platelets (**3**) are tiny discs that seal tears or cuts in damaged blood vessels. They also produce substances that make blood clot. Clotting stops an injured person bleeding to death.

Blood facts and figures

- An adult man is likely to contain 5 litres (1 gallon) of blood.
- About 55 per cent of blood is plasma.
- About 90 per cent of plasma is water.
- A healthy adult contains about 20,000 billion red blood cells.
- Blood contains over 500 times more red cells and 25 times more platelets than white cells.
- Red blood cells live about 17 weeks.
- The body destroys about 120 million old red blood cells every minute.

Blood inside the body

When someone rests blood is distributed around the body like this (in exercise the pattern changes):

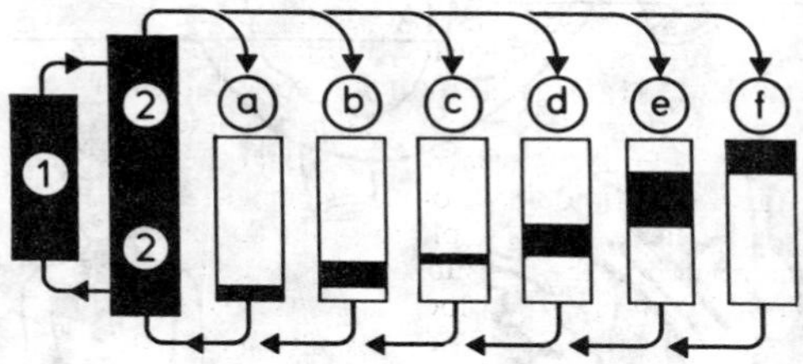

1 Lungs
2 Heart (left/right sides)
a Skeleton, skin, etc, 10%
b Brain 15%
c Heart blood vessels 5%
d Muscles 15%
e Intestines 35%
f Kidneys 20%

Heart

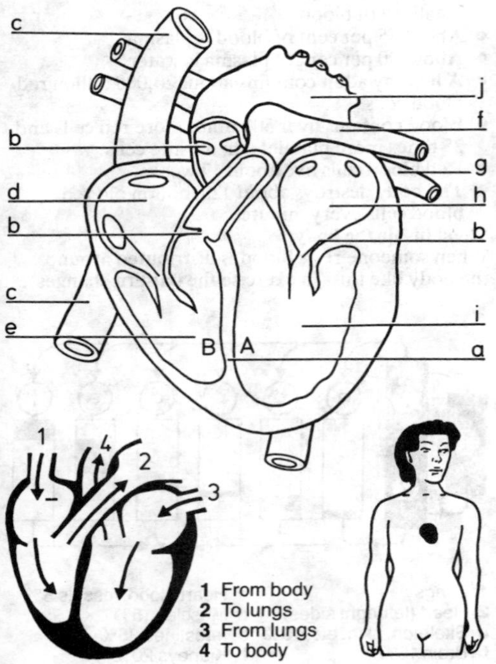

1 From body
2 To lungs
3 From lungs
4 To body

This muscular pump drives blood around the body. The heart's non-stop action supplies oxygen and nutrients to body cells, and removes their waste products.

Structure The heart is a fist-sized hollow muscle with a broad top and pointed base. It lies roughly in the middle of the chest. A wall called a septum (**a**) divides the right side (**A**) from the left side (**B**). Each side has an inlet, outlet, and two chambers: atrium and ventricle. Valves (**b**) control the blood flow in and out.

How it works The heart works as two pumps. As the heart relaxes blood flows into both atria. As the atria contract, blood flows through valves into the ventricles. Lastly, the ventricles contract, forcing blood out of the heart.

Deoxygenated blood from the body flows via the superior vena cava and inferior vena cava (**c**) into the right atrium (**d**) and right ventricle (**e**) then out through the pulmonary artery (**f**) to the lungs. Oxygenated blood from the lungs flows via the pulmonary vein (**g**) into the left atrium (**h**) and left ventricle (**i**) then out through the aorta (**j**) to the body.

Each complete contraction produces one heartbeat. Nerve signals to the heart keep heartbeats regular. But heartbeats speed up during exercise as the heart pumps faster and harder to satisfy the body's extra needs for blood and oxygen.

Circulation
Here we show in schematic form the flow of blood around the body to and from the heart.

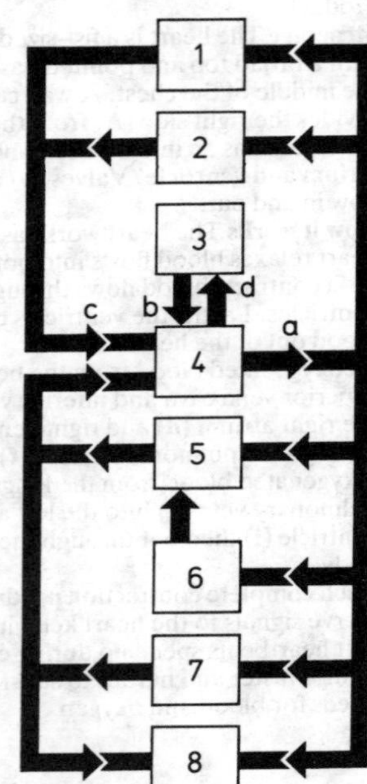

1 Head
2 Arms
3 Lungs
4 Heart
5 Liver
6 Intestine
7 Kidneys
8 Legs
a Aorta (main artery)
b Pulmonary vein
c Superior and inferior vena cava (main veins)
d Pulmonary artery

Arteries and veins

These are the largest blood vessels. Arteries (**1**) are large tubes carrying high-pressure blood away from the heart. They have thick, muscular walls. Arteries branch into countless tiny tubes called arterioles. Veins (**2**) are large tubes that return low-pressure blood to the heart. Veins have thinner walls than arteries. Veins are supplied by tiny blood vessels called venules. The tiniest blood vessels are capillaries. Capillaries (**3**) link arterioles and venules.

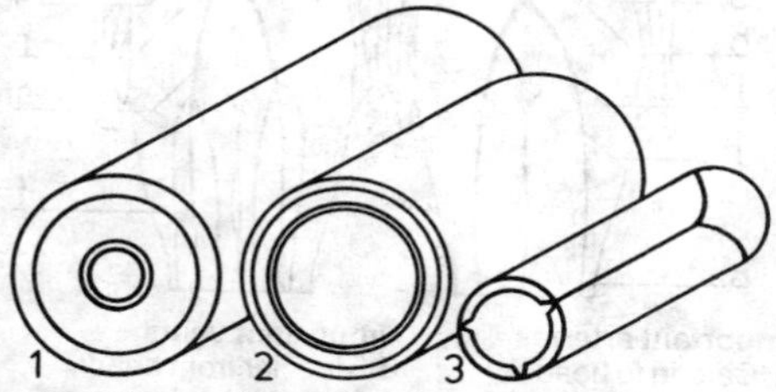

The heart's pumping action forces blood out through arteries into arterioles and capillaries. Foods in the blood pass out through capillaries' walls to nourish surrounding tissues. Wastes pass in through the walls, and oxygen enters capillaries next to the lungs. From capillaries, blood flows back to the heart through the venules and veins. Muscles near veins keep this blood on the move, and valves in big veins stop blood sinking back down in the legs and feet.

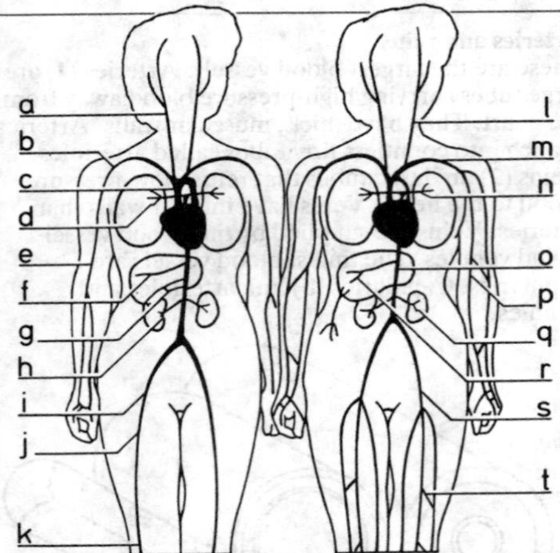

Important arteries

a Carotid to head
b Subclavian to arm
c Aorta supplying all but lungs
d Pulmonary to lungs
e Brachial in arm
f Hepatic to liver
g Gastric to stomach
h Renal to kidney
i Iliac to thigh
j Femoral in thigh
k Tibial in leg

Important veins

l Jugular from head
m Subclavian from arm
n Pulmonary from lung
o Superior and inferior vena cava from all but lungs
p Brachial in arm
q Hepatic from liver
r Renal from kidney
s Iliac from thigh
t Femoral in thigh

Taking your pulse
Each heartbeat sends a wave through your arteries. You can feel this by pressing fingers on the underside of your forearm behind the base of the thumb. Count the beats for 15 seconds and multiply by four to find the pulse rate per minute. For most adults the pulse rate is about 70, but it is more rapid in children and slower in elderly people. Pulse rate increases with exercise.

Blood pressure
This is the pressure exerted by blood on artery walls. It varies with how fast and hard the heart beats, and with the condition of arteries.
Blood pressure is measured with a sphygmomanometer. This instrument shows the pressure needed to stop blood flowing through an artery in the arm. Systolic pressure (pressure when the heart contracts) and diastolic pressure (pressure when the heart relaxes) are given in millimetres. Normal blood pressure for adults is about 120/80.

Lymphatic system
This is a body-wide network of vessels that traps fluid escaped from blood vessels, and returns it to the blood supply. That stops tissues swelling. The system also absorbs harmful bacteria and other dangerous substances.

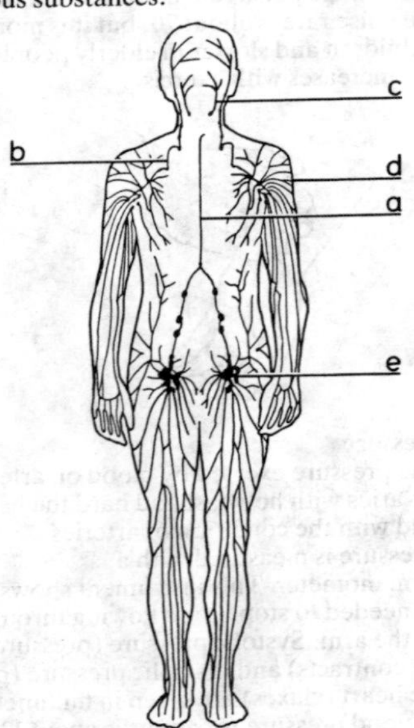

How it works Blood pressure forces fluid from tiny blood vessels into surrounding tissues. Most fluid finds its way into tiny blood vessels, but some enters the lymph vessels. It flows towards the thoracic duct or to the right lymphatic duct. The forces that drive it are muscle activity and pulsating blood vessels. Most lymph travels upwards; valves in lymph vessels prevent it flowing back down. From the thoracic duct lymph drains back into the blood supply near the left shoulder. From the right lymphatic duct lymph drains back into the bloodstream near the right shoulder.
Structure The lymphatic system is like a system of rivers and tributaries. Instead of water all contain lymph, a salty straw-coloured liquid like the fluid part of blood, but with less protein. The system's many tiny vessels join to form a few large ones. Largest of all is the thoracic duct (**a**) which runs up the body in front of the spine. Another large vessel, the right lymphatic duct (**b**), runs through the right arm and shoulder. Bumpy swellings called lymph nodes occur in neck (**c**), armpits (**d**), above the groin (**e**), and elsewhere. These contain white cells that absorb harmful substances such as bacteria. (See **Body defences**.)

Lymph circulation
a Heart
b Artery
c Capillaries
d Vein
e Lymph duct

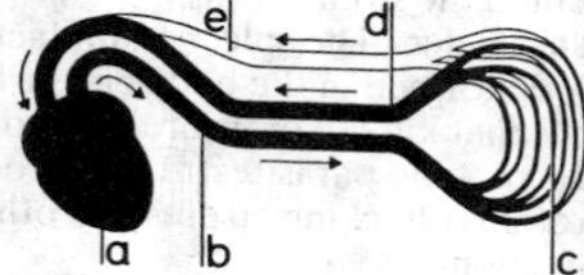

Spleen
This organ plays a part in circulation and combating infection.

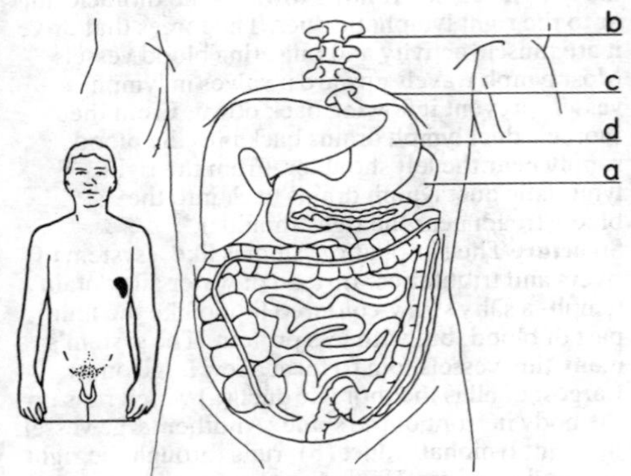

Structure and location The spleen is a spongy, fist-sized purplish object (**a**) located just in front of the spine (**b**), below the diaphragm (**c**), and left of and behind the stomach (**d**).
What it does The spleen manufactures some of the blood formed in the body before birth. It contains cells that kill old or injured blood cells and destroy bacteria and parasites. It also produces antibodies: proteins attacking viruses and other agents of infection.

Digestive system

This system's organs break down food into molecules the body can absorb and use for building and repair and as a source of energy.

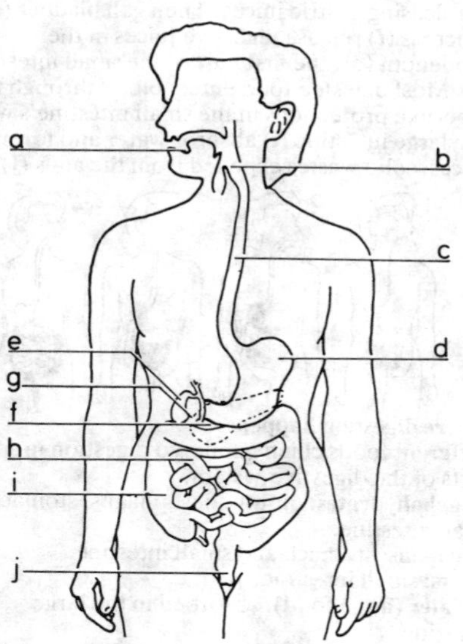

Structures and processes Digestion happens in the alimentary canal, a tube 9m (30ft) long with different parts. Waves of movement in its walls force food along. Food entering the mouth (**a**) is swallowed by the pharynx (**b**), then passes through the gullet or oesophagus (**c**), to the stomach (**d**). This muscular bag churns food and dissolves some by releasing gastric juices. Then gall bladder (**e**) and pancreas (**f**) release digestive juices in the duodenum (**g**), the first part of the small intestine (**h**). Most digested food enters blood through tiny fingerlike projections in the small intestine's walls. The large intestine (**i**) absorbs water and forms faeces, solid wastes expelled from the anus (**j**).

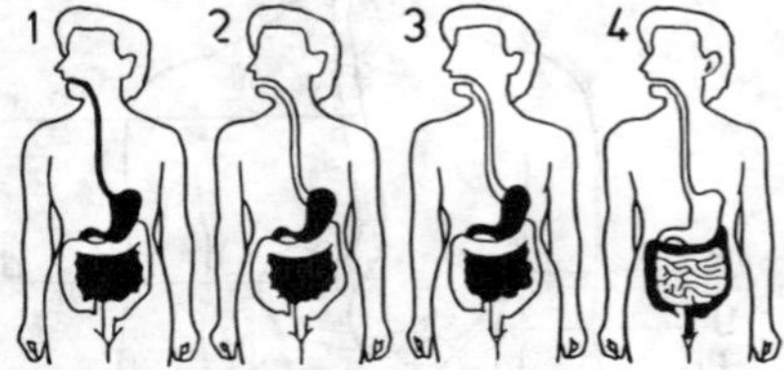

Where digestion happens
Different foods chiefly undergo digestion in specific parts of the digestive system.
1 Carbohydrates: mouth, oesophagus, stomach, small intestine.
2 Proteins: stomach and small intestine.
3 Fats: small intestine.
4 Water (not a food): absorbed in the large intestine.

Mouth

The mouth takes in food and starts the process of digestion. Lips (**a**) help us drink and bring food inside the mouth. Teeth (**b**) break food into smaller pieces (see also pages 98–100). Salivary glands (**c**) produce saliva that moistens and softens food and begins digesting starches. The bony hard palate (**d**) and the soft palate (**e**) stop food entering and blocking the airway through the nose and upper throat or pharynx. The tongue (**f**) helps to form each mouthful into a ball or bolus, then moves it back into the throat for swallowing.

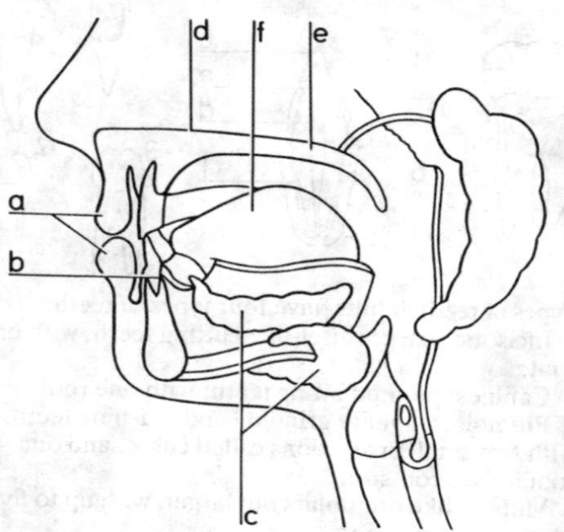

Teeth
Teeth are hard bonelike projections set in sockets in the jaws. Teeth bite and chew food into smaller pieces as a first stage in food digestion.
Structure Each tooth has a visible crown (**a**) rising from one or more roots (**b**) hidden by the gums and embedded in the jaw. The crown has a very hard, smooth, shiny outer layer of enamel (**c**). The root is covered by bone-hard cementum (**d**). Inside the tooth, hard yellow dentine (**e**) surrounds soft pulp (**f**) containing nerves, blood vessels, and connective tissue.

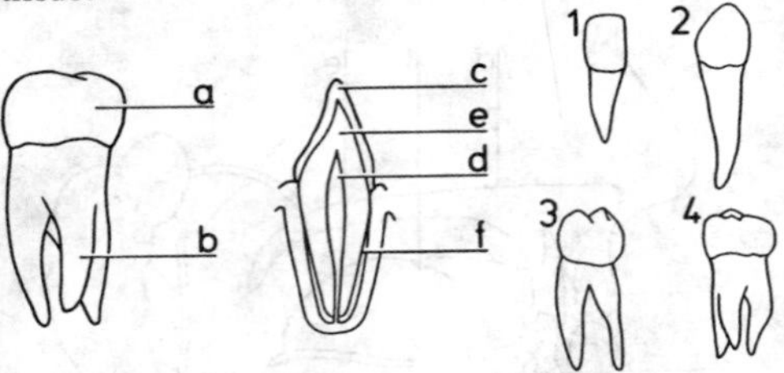

Types of teeth Adults have four types of teeth:
1 Incisors: sharp, chisel-like cutting teeth, with one root.
2 Canines: pointed biting teeth, with one root.
3 Premolars: square grinding and crushing teeth, with two small projections called cusps, and one root or two roots.
4 Molars: like premolars but larger, with up to five cusps and three roots.

Primary or milk teeth By about the age of two most children have gained 20 teeth: 8 incisors, 4 canines, and 8 molars.

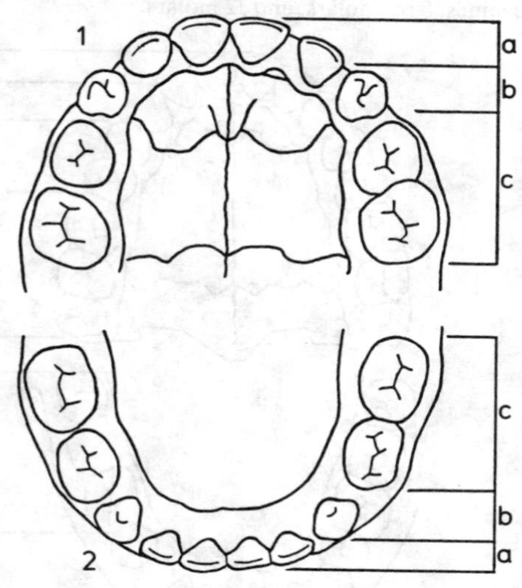

1 Upper teeth
2 Lower teeth
a Incisors
b Canines
c Molars

Permanent teeth These start replacing primary teeth by about the age of six, and by about the age of 20 most adults have 32 permanent teeth: 8 incisors, 4 canines, 8 premolars, and 12 molars.

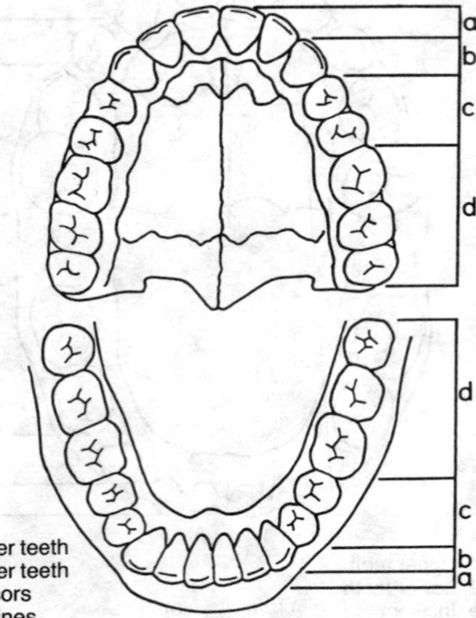

Stomach

This baglike organ stores food and helps digest it. An adult stomach holds about 1.1 litres (2 pints).

Structure The stomach (**a**) is a J-shaped bag in the upper left abdomen between the oesophagus (**b**) and duodenum (**c**). Its wall has three muscular layers: circular (**d**), longitudinal (**e**), and oblique (**f**).

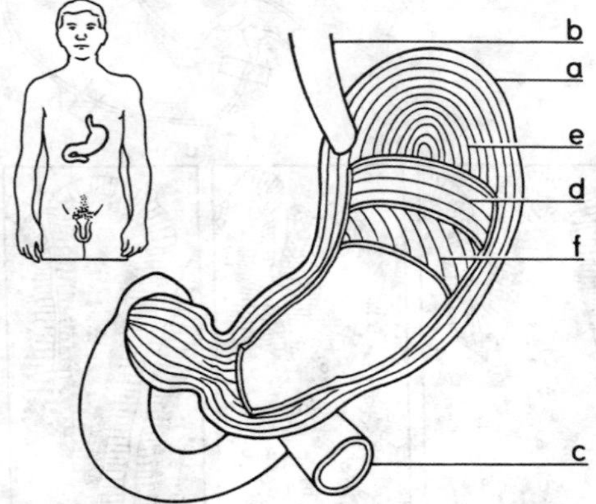

How the stomach works Muscular contractions mix food with the stomach juices. Hydrochloric acid kills germs and pepsin digests protein. Mucus protects the stomach lining from the acid. Liquidized food (called chyme) slowly empties from the stomach into the small intestine.

Stomach lining Different parts of the stomach lining have special cells producing different substances:

a Cardia: sticky mucus
b Fundus: pepsin and hydrochloric acid
c Pylorus: sticky mucus

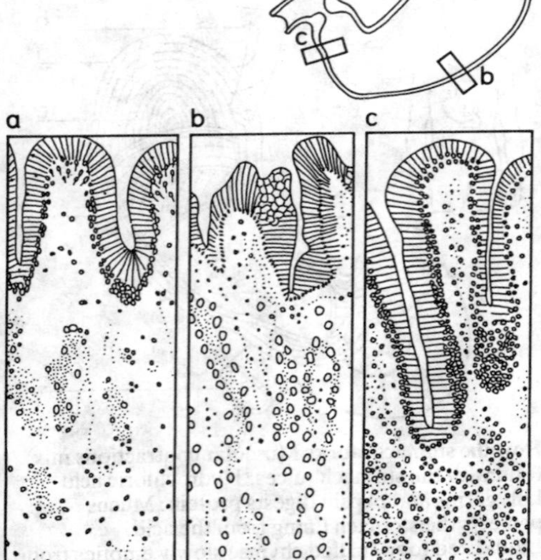

Intestine
This muscular tube digests food, expels solid body wastes, and absorbs water.

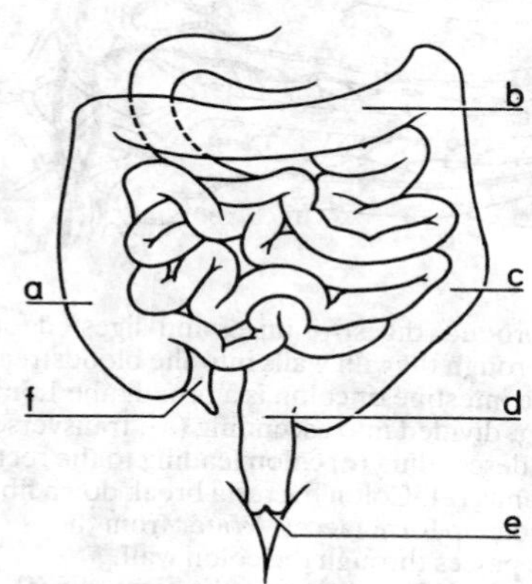

Structure The intestine is a convoluted tube in the abdomen (belly). Its two parts are the small and large intestine (**1**).
The small intestine is a narrow tube about 6.5m (21ft) long between the stomach and the large intestine, and divided into (upper) duodenum, (middle) jejunum, and (lower) ileum. Its inner wall is lined with billions of microscopic fingerlike projections (**2**). Spread flat, these villi and microvilli would cover an area 200 times the size of the skin.

2

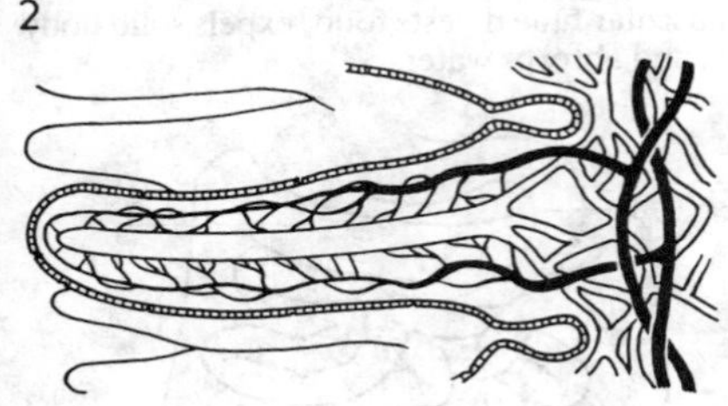

Glands produce digestive juices and digested food passes through the villi walls into the bloodstream. The large intestine or colon is a broad tube 1.5m (5ft) long, divided into ascending (**a**), transverse (**b**), and descending (**c**) colon leading to the rectum (**d**) and anus (**e**). Colon bacteria break down fibrous foods and help form faeces. Water from the intestine passes through the colon wall.
A short, wormlike cul-de-sac, the appendix (**f**), branches off the beginning of the colon. It serves no obviously useful purpose.

Gall bladder

This little bag stores bile, a substance produced by the liver. Bile helps to break down fats during digestion.

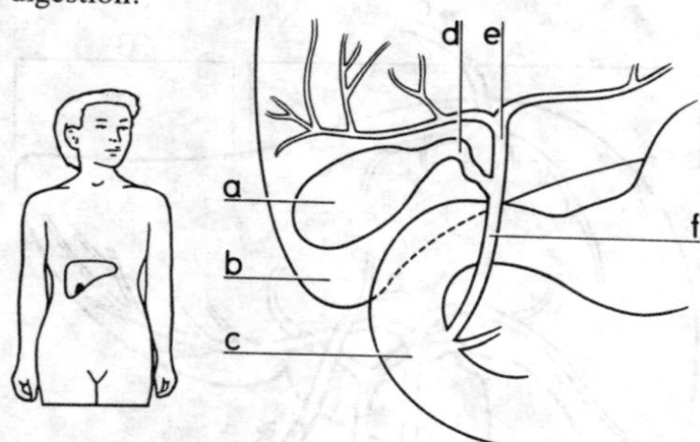

Structure The gall bladder (**a**) is a pear-shaped bag under the right lobe of the liver (**b**) and near the duodenum (**c**), the upper end of the small intestine. A tube called the cystic duct (**d**) joins the bag's narrow end to the bile (hepatic) duct (**e**), a tube from the liver. Both lead on to the common bile duct (**f**), a tube that opens into the duodenum.

How it works Between meals, the common bile duct's mouth closes, and bile coming from the liver backs up in the gall bladder. This bag can hold about 43ml (1½oz) of bile. When the stored bile is needed, the common bile duct's mouth opens and bile escapes from the gall bladder into the duodenum.

Liver
The largest gland in the body, the liver is a complex chemical factory and an important food store.

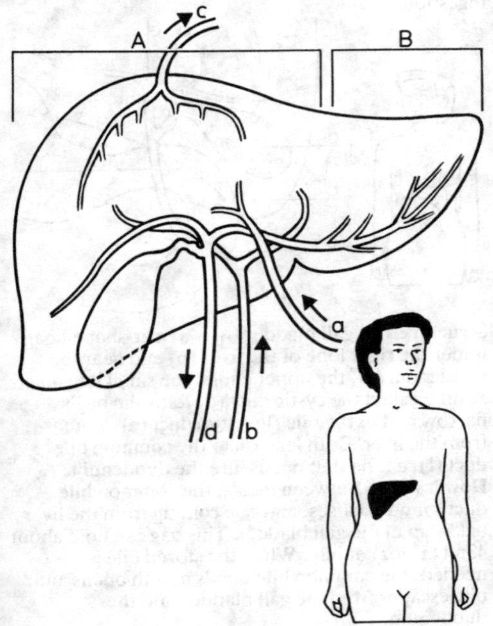

Structure The liver forms a spongy reddish mass in the right upper abdomen. It weighs 1.4kg (3lb) and has four lobes: right (**A**), left (**B**) and two small lobes behind the right. These hold altogether up to 100,000 lobules. Each lobule contains groups of specialized liver cells. Between groups of liver cells are tiny caverns called sinusoids.
How it works Inside the lobules, sinusoids fill with blood from two sources. The hepatic artery (**a**) brings blood and oxygen from the heart. The portal vein (**b**) brings nutrient-rich blood from the small intestine. Liver cells absorb nutrients and oxygen from the blood, cleanse it of poisons and wastes, and enrich the blood with sugar, minerals, and vitamins. Processed in these ways, blood leaves the liver by way of the hepatic vein (**c**).
Liver cells also produce bile, a substance that breaks down fats in the small intestine. Bile leaves the liver through the bile (hepatic) duct (**d**). (See also **gall bladder**.)
Chief uses The liver makes certain blood proteins. It controls the body's chief fuel supply (glucose) by storing surplus glucose as glycogen and reconverting it to glucose when required. It stores certain vitamins, iron, and minerals. It breaks down wastes into soluble products that can be expelled via the kidneys.

Urinary system

Kidneys

Kidneys are a pair of organs for filtering impurities from blood. They prevent poisons fatally accumulating in the body.

Structure Kidneys are two bean-shaped objects behind the stomach, one on each side of the spine. Together, kidneys add up to the same size as the heart. Each kidney has three layers. From the outside in these are the cortex (**a**), medulla (**b**), and pelvis (**c**). Cortex and medulla contain tiny blood filtration units called nephrons (**d**). (A single kidney has more than a million nephrons.) Urine, the waste product of filtration, collects in the kidney's pelvis.

How they work Blood for processing enters the medulla from the renal artery (**e**). Inside the medulla and cortex, the artery splits into tiny coiled

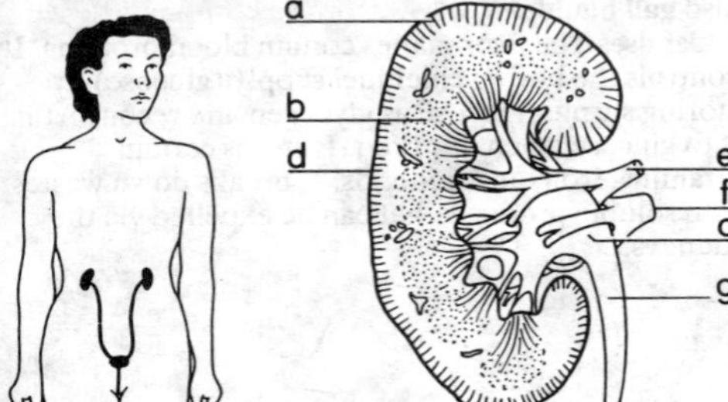

blood vessels. Each coiled vessel is called a glomerulus (**h**). Almost completely surrounding this lies a pinhead-sized sac called a Bowman's capsule (**i**). Pressure forces water and dissolved chemicals from the blood in the glomerulus into the Bowman's capsule. The filtered liquid then continues through a tubule (**j**) surrounded by capillaries (**k**). These tiny blood vessels reabsorb into the blood most of the water and such useful chemicals as amino acids. The treated blood then leaves the kidney via the renal vein (**f**).

Meanwhile, wastes remaining in the convoluted tubule flow on via a collecting tubule to the kidney's pelvis. These wastes now form urine, an amber liquid largely made of water, uric acid, urea, and inorganic salts. From the kidney's pelvis, urine leaves the kidney through a tube known as a ureter (**g**). (See also **bladder**.)

One pair of kidneys can process 190 litres (42 gallons) of blood a day. Their urine output drops in sleep or during perspiration, and rises after someone has been drinking more liquid than usual.

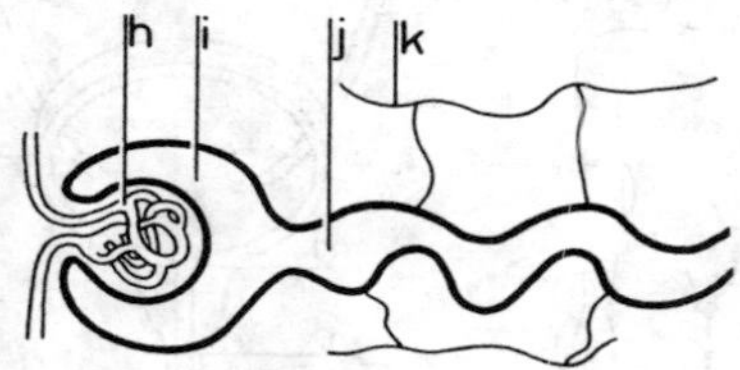

Bladder
The urinary bladder is a bag for storing urine before it leaves the body.
Structure The bladder is a hollow, muscular bag lying just behind the hip bone called the pubis. Two macaroni-thick tubes called ureters (**a**) connect the bladder (**b**) to the kidneys. A broader tube, the urethra (**d**) opens from the bottom of the bladder. A ring of muscles called the urethal sphincter (**c**) normally keeps this outlet closed.
An empty bladder is flat. A full bladder can hold about 0.5 litre (a pint) of urine.
How it works Urine drips into the bladder through the ureters. The bladder's walls relax as it fills. When the bladder holds about a cupful of urine, nerves start sending the brain 'urinate' signals. Urination occurs when the urethral sphincter relaxes and the bladder wall contracts, forcing urine out through the urethra.

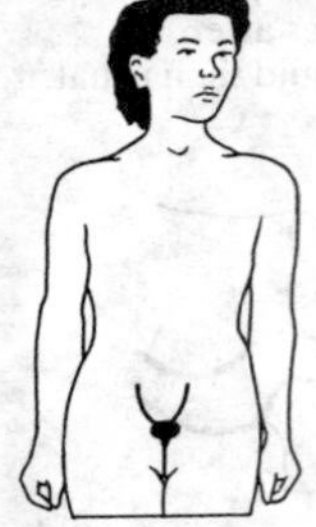

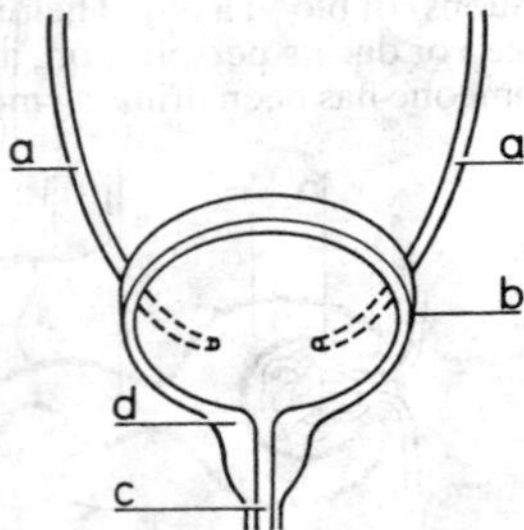

Endocrine system

Exocrine glands
Exocrine glands produce substances released via ducts to other organs or the surface of the skin. Some also work in other ways. Here are some major types of exocrine glands and their products.

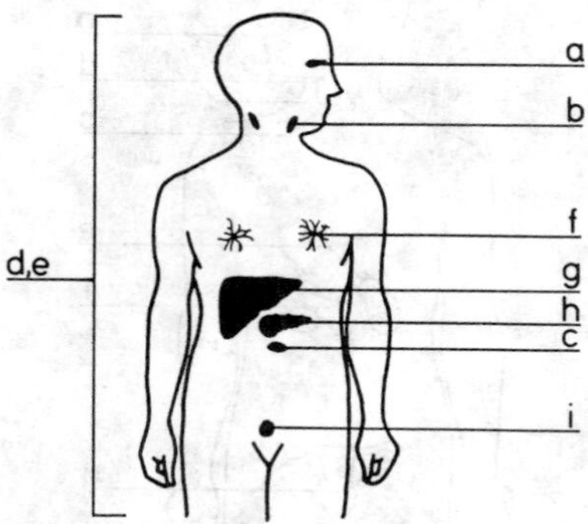

a Lacrimal glands (tears)
b Salivary glands (saliva)
c Mucus glands (mucus)
d Sweat glands of skin (sweat)
e Sebaceous glands of skin (sebum)
f Mammary glands in women (milk)
g Liver (bile)
h Pancreas (digestive juices.)
i Prostate in men (seminal fluid)

Endocrine system

Endocrine glands release into the blood hormones ('chemical messengers') that reach target glands and organs to control growth, reproduction, and daily processes of living. Here are some major endocrine glands described on the next pages or elsewhere.

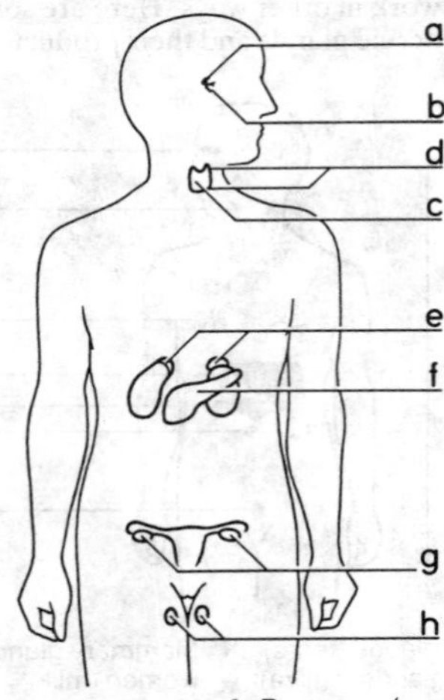

a Hypothalamus
b Pituitary
c Thyroid
d Parathyroid glands
e Adrenal gland
f Pancreas (contains some endocrine cells)
g Ovaries in females
h Testicles in males

Hypothalamus and pituitary
The hypothalamus in the brain controls some body functions through nerve mechanisms, but many more via the pituitary gland, 'leader of the endocrine orchestra'.

Structure Nerve tissue (**a**) links the thumb-tip size hypothalamus (**b**) to the pea-sized pituitary (**c**), comprising posterior (**d**) and anterior (**e**) lobes.

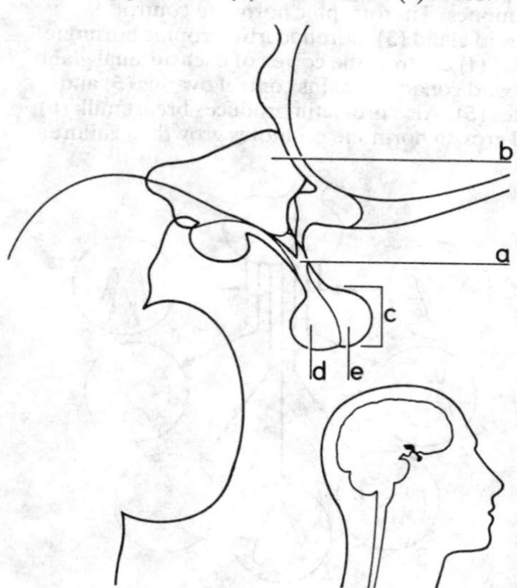

How they work The hypothalamus produces the hormones vasopressin (ADP) and oxytocin, stored and released by the pituitary's posterior lobe. Vasopressin (ADP) controls water output of the kidneys (**1**) and during birth, oxytocin produces contractions of the uterus (**2**).
Releasing hormones from the hypothalamus make the pituitary's anterior lobe produce other hormones: Thyrotrophic hormone controls the thyroid gland (**3**), adrenocorticotrophic hormone (ACTH) controls the cortex of each adrenal gland (**4**), and gonadotrophins control ovaries (**5**) and testes (**5**). Also prolactin produces breast milk (**6**) and growth hormone promotes growth in children (**7**).

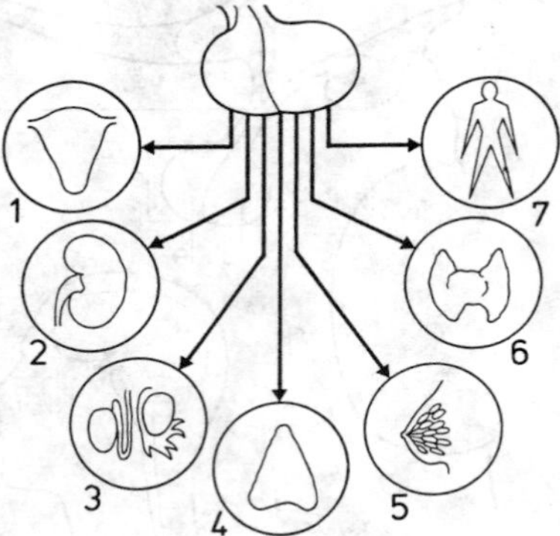

Thyroid gland

This gland weighs about 28g (1oz). It lies in the neck, wrapped around the front of the windpipe, with a large lobe on either side. Thyrotrophin (TSH) hormone from the pituitary gland stimulates the thyroid to produce thyroxine and triiodothyronine which regulate growth and mental development, and calcitonin, which helps build bone.

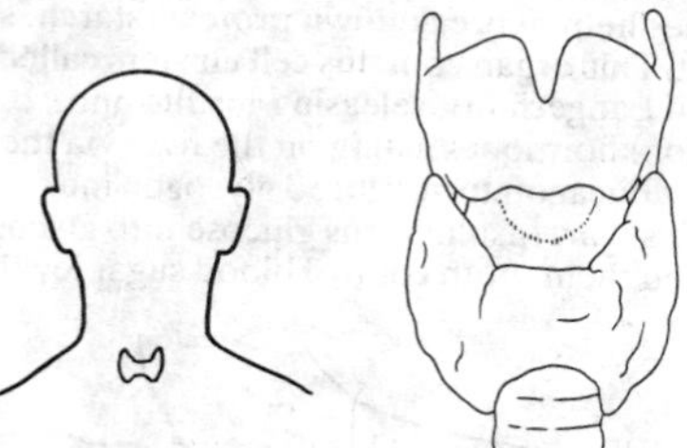

Parathyroid glands

Each of these four tiny glands is about 6mm (¼in) across. They lie in (sometimes near) the thyroid's lobes and produce parathormone. This hormone keeps up the blood's level of calcium by taking some from bone.

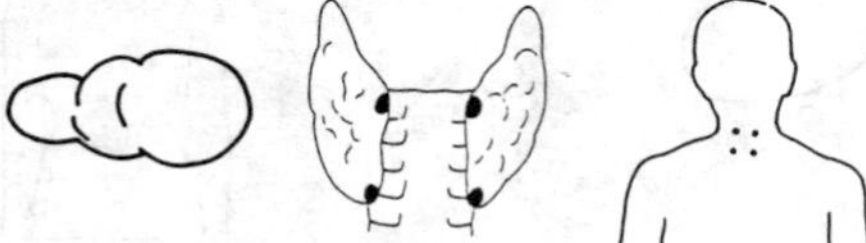

Pancreas

The pancreas produces substances that help to break down foodstuffs in digestion, and controls the amount of sugar in the blood.

Structure This is a soft, leaf-shaped organ about 18cm (7in) long and 2.5cm (1in) thick, below the stomach. A tube connects it to the duodenum.

What it does The pancreas releases enzymes through its duct into the duodenum. There the enzymes help to break down protein, starch, sugar, and fat. This organ contains cell clusters called the islets of Langerhans, releasing insulin and glucagon: hormones acting on the liver via the blood. Glucagon turns stored glycogen into glucose sugar. Insulin turns glucose into glycogen. Between them, both control blood sugar level.

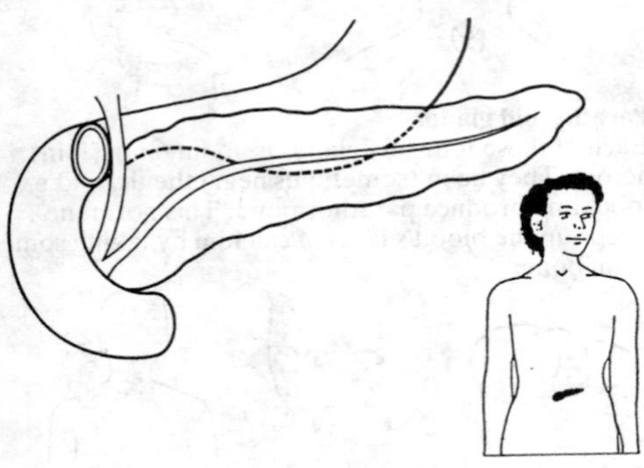

Adrenal glands
These two triangular objects about 5cm (2in) across sit on the kidneys. Adrenals have a cortex (**a**) and medulla (**b**). The cortex yields corticosteroid hormones; glucocorticoids (e.g. cortisol) dealing with sugar and stress), mineralocorticoids (e.g. aldosterone) keeping salt in the body, and sex hormones (especially the male hormones androgens). The medulla (under nervous-system control) produces adrenalin, which speeds up bloodflow under stress.

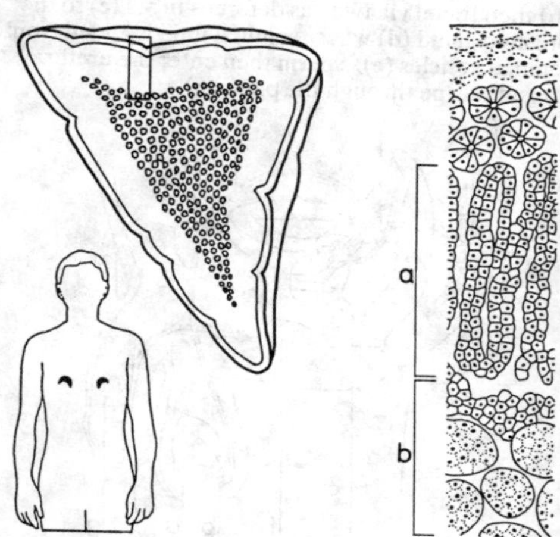

Reproductive system

Male sex organs
A man's sex organs produce the minute tadpole-shaped sex cells called sperm. A sperm that fertilizes an egg produces an embryo that develops into a baby.

Structures and functions Sperm are produced in two testes (**a**): endocrine glands hung in a pouch, the scrotum. Sperm cells develop in the epididymides (**b**) then travel via two vas deferens tubes (**c**) to the prostate gland (**d**) where seminal fluid is added from seminal vesicles (**e**). Sperm then enter the urethra (**f**) and escape through the penis (**g**).

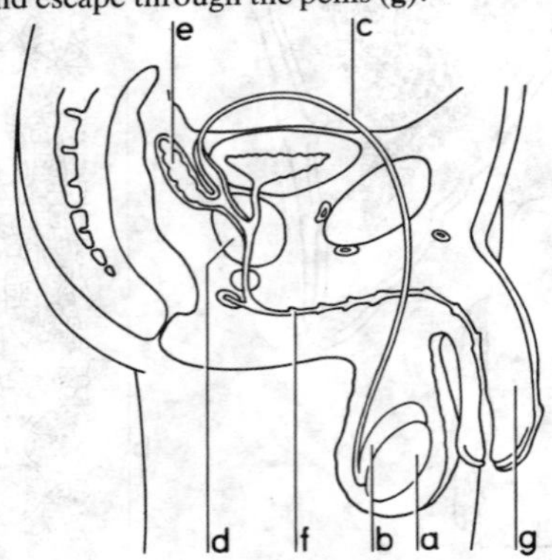

Female sex organs
A woman's reproductive system produces eggs and babies and provides these with nourishment.
Main structures The vagina (**a**) is a muscular tube opening between the rectum and urethra. A narrow neck, the cervix (**b**), leads to the womb or uterus (**c**), a hollow, muscular organ as big as a pear. Fallopian tubes (**d**) connect the uterus to the ovaries (**e**), where the eggs are produced. Breasts (**f**) are milk-producing glands.

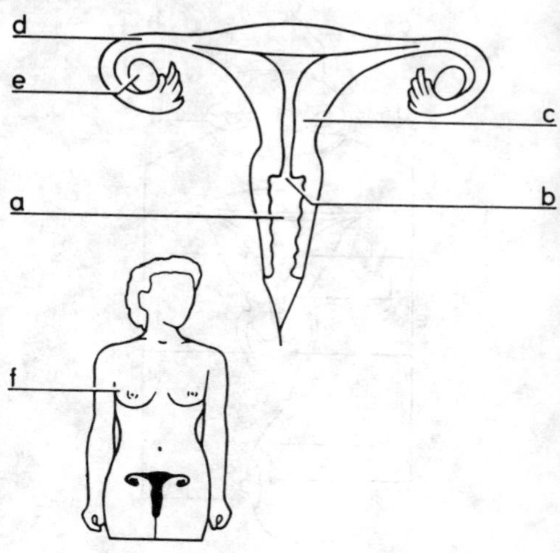

Menstrual cycle
Menstruation is a woman's monthly 'period' when the vagina discharges blood and mucus. This happens as part of the 28-day menstrual cycle of egg production controlled by a hormone feedback

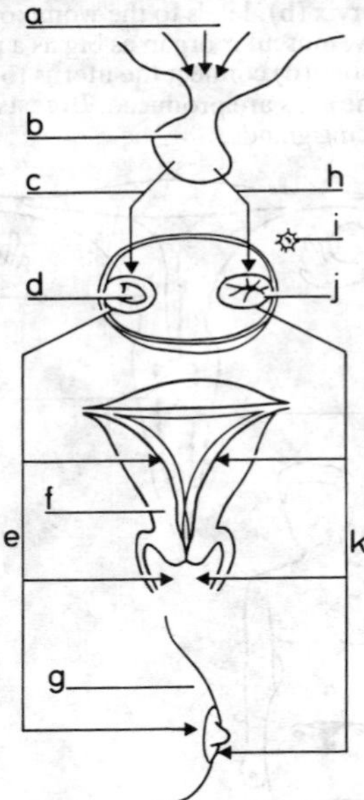

system run by the hypothalamus (**a**) and pituitary (**b**) in the brain.

From day 1: Follicle stimulating hormone or FSH (**c**) helps a new egg form in an egg follicle (**d**).

From day 4: The follicle produces oestrogen (**e**) promoting growth of the uterus (**f**) and breasts (**g**), releasing luteinizing hormone or LH (**h**), and blocking FSH output.

From day 12: LH bursts the follicle, releasing an egg or ovum (**i**) and transforming the follicle into a corpus luteum (**j**) yielding estrogen and progesterone (**k**).

From day 14: Progesterone prepares the uterus wall to receive a fertilized egg. If fertilization fails to occur, the corpus luteum shrinks, LH, oestrogen, and progesterone output fall, the uterus lining breaks up and its bloody fragments escape in the monthly menstrual discharge.

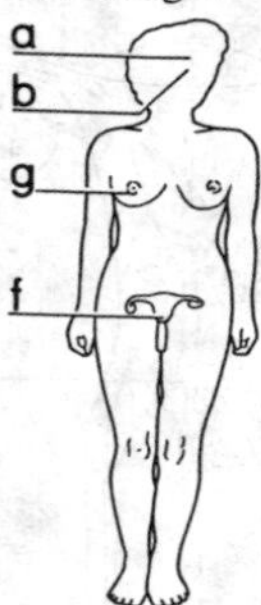

Conception

A new life starts when a sperm fertilizes an egg. During sexual intercourse, a man's penis releases millions of sperms into a woman's vagina (**a**). Lashed along by their tails, the microscopic sperms wriggle through the cervix (**b**), a narrow neck, into the womb or uterus (**c**).

Fewer than 3000 sperms probably survive to continue on into the two fallopian tubes (**d**). If the woman has recently ovulated (released an egg or ovum from an ovary) some sperms may find an egg (**e**) already in a tube. If egg release has not occurred, the sperms can survive up to three days until an egg arrives.

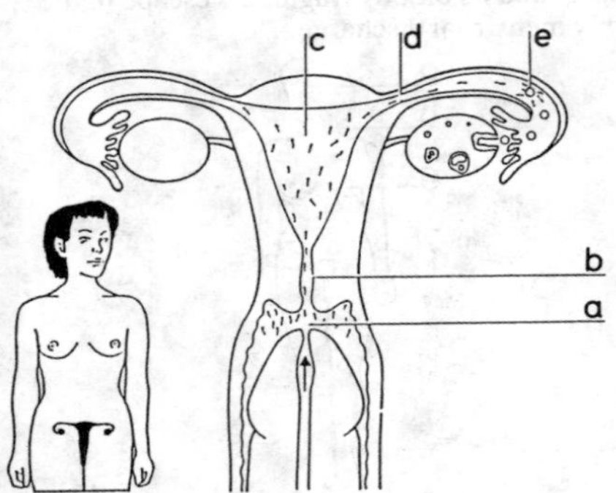

Fertilization

Hugely magnified, a tadpole-like sperm (**a**) fertilizes an egg or ovum (**b**) much larger than itself. The sperm's tail will fall off but its head or nucleus will fuse with the ovum nucleus. The ovum then gains a hardened wall to keep out other sperms.

From puberty to old age, men's testes produce 10–30 billion sperms a month. Women are born with perhaps 350,000 immature eggs. Between puberty and menopause, at least one egg matures in an ovary each month and is released for possible fertilization. Only some 375 eggs mature throughout a lifetime.

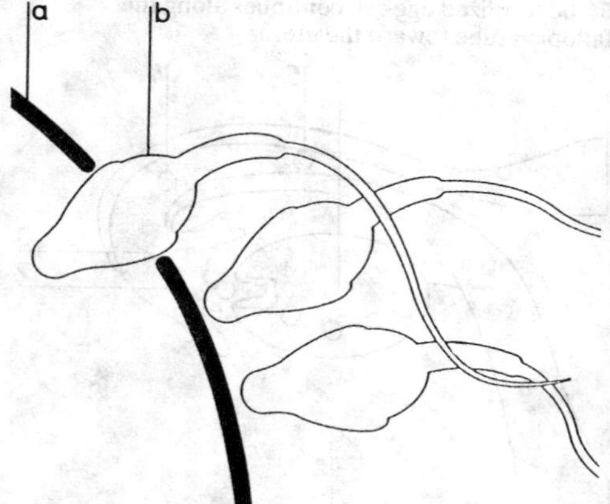

Implantation
A diagram shows processes leading to implantation of a fertilized egg in the uterus.
1 Several ova (eggs) are developing in follicles (sacs) in an ovary.
2 A mature ovum (egg) is released from the ovary into a fallopian tube by the process called ovulation. The ovum nucleus then splits in two.
3 The smaller part (polar body) of the ovum nucleus moves to the ovum shell.
4 The nucleus splits again, and a second polar body moves to the ovum shell. At this point a sperm fuses with the main nucleus to fertilize the egg.
5 The fertilized egg cell continues along the fallopian tube toward the uterus.

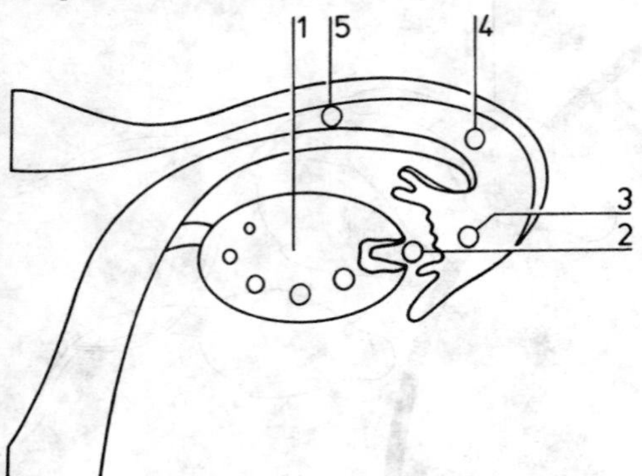

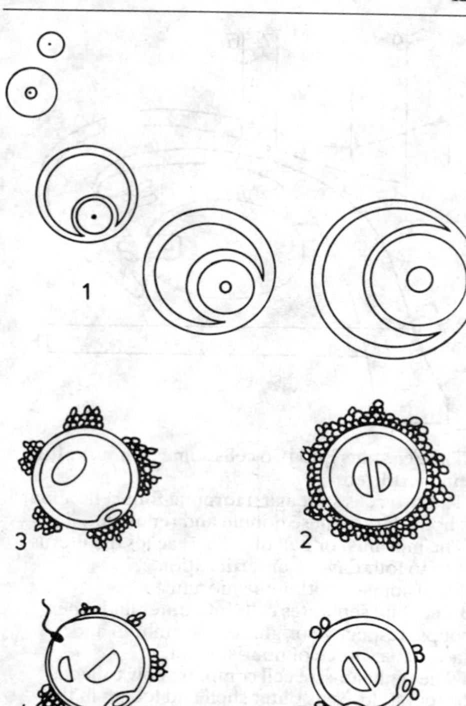
1
3
2
4
5

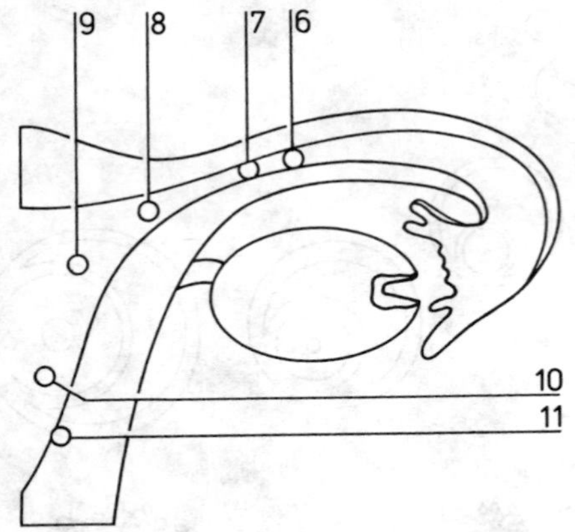

6 The egg splits into two cells some 30 hours after being fertilized.
7 The two cells split again forming four cells about 20 hours later. These double and redouble.
8 The morulus, or ball of cells, reaches the uterus three to four days after fertilization.
9 Fluid appears within the morulus.
10 The fluid separates cells into outer and inner groups, respective origins of the embryo and placenta, a source of nourishment.
11 The pinhead-size cell complex, now called a blastocyst, loses its outer shell and lodges in the uterus wall.

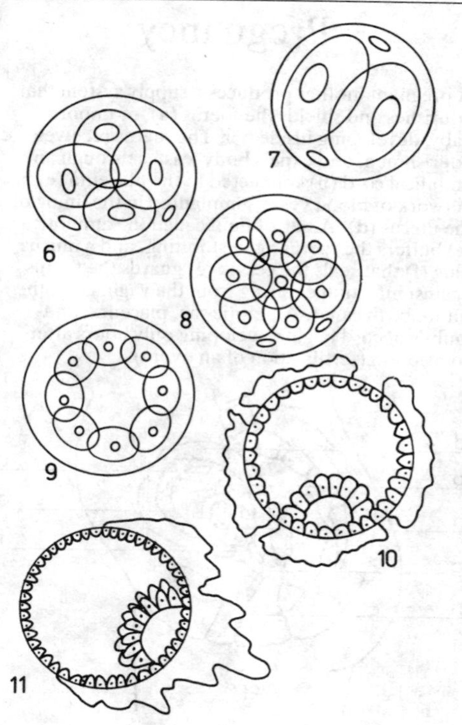
6
7
8
9
10
11

Pregnancy

A pregnant mother produces a supply system that nourishes and shields the foetus (**a**), or unborn baby, developing inside her. The foetus receives nourishment and expels body wastes through an umbilical cord (**b**) connected to the placenta (**c**), a network of blood vessels implanted in the lining of the uterus (**d**). A bag of fluid called the amniotic sac (**e**) buffers the foetus against jolting, and a mucus plug (**f**) that seals the cervix (**g**) guards the foetus against infection entering from the vagina (**h**), the future birth canal. Amniotic sac, placenta, and umbilical cord begin developing only hours after conception (fertilization of an ovum).

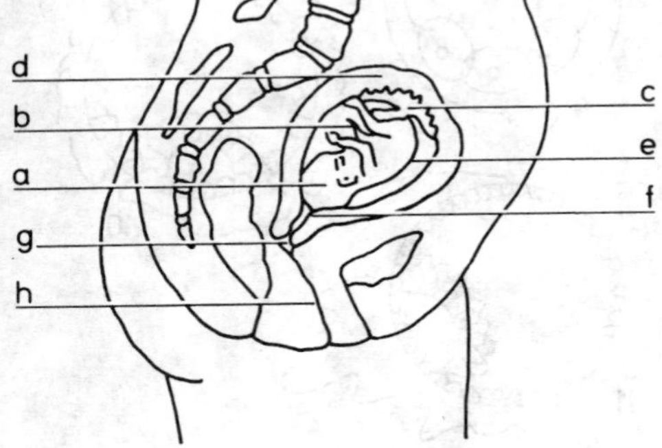

Weeks 1 to 11
Pregnancy lasts 40 weeks, counting from the first day of the last menstrual period. We show the first 11 weeks of a developing egg and embryo (not to scale). Lengths and weights can vary. By 11 weeks, an embryo no longer than a thumb already has a human appearance, with head, body, and limbs.
Weeks 2–3 After ovulation and fertilization, the ovum becomes implanted in the uterus wall.
Week 4 The fertilized egg develops basic structures and is called an embryo.
Week 5 The embryo is 2mm (0.08in) long. It has a bulge (a future head with embryonic brain), a middle with a simple heart, and a tail.

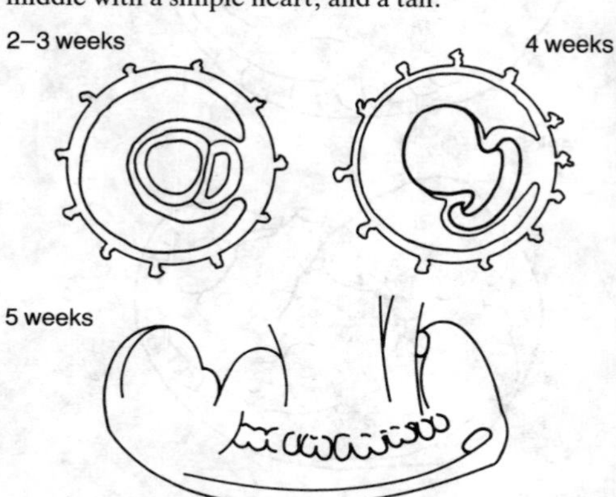

Week 6 The embryo is 6mm (0.23in) long, with limb buds, and rudimentary chest and abdomen.
Week 7 The embryo is 1.3cm (0.5in) long, with limbs, and beginnings of ears, eyes, intestines, kidneys, liver, lungs, mouth, nostrils, and nervous system.

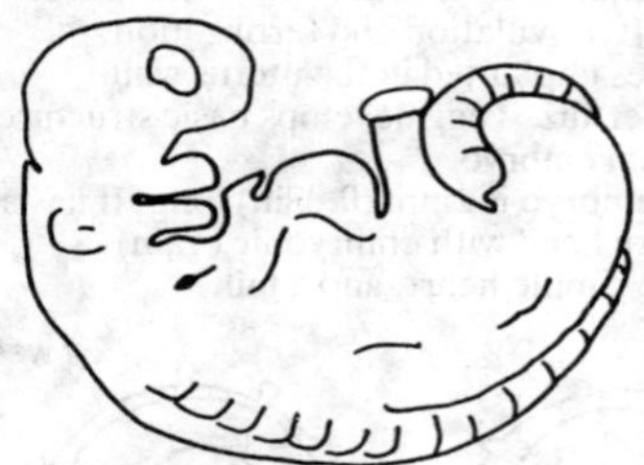

6 weeks

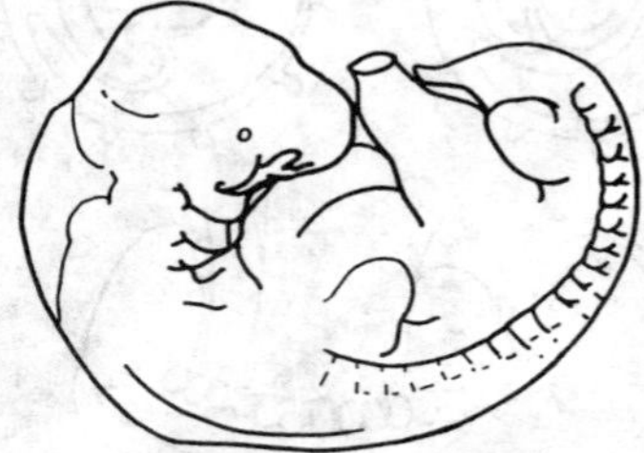

7 weeks

Week 9 The embryo is 3cm (1.2in) long and weighs 2gm (0.07oz). It has immature internal organs and rudimentary fingers and toes.
Week 11 The embryo is 5.5cm (2.6in) long and weighs 10gm (0.35oz). It has obvious facial features, a rounded head, and internal ovaries or testes.

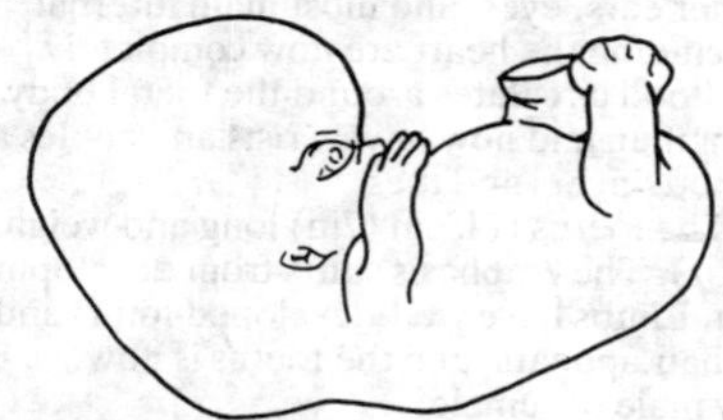

9 weeks

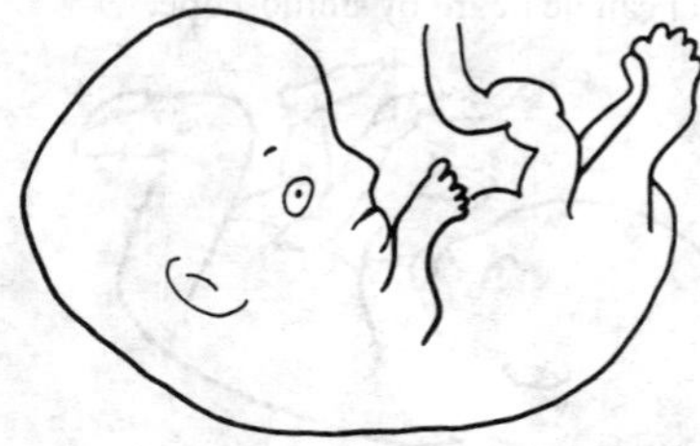

11 weeks

Weeks 12–26
Illustrations show changes in the foetus at intervals during the middle weeks of pregnancy.

Week 12 The foetus is 9cm (3.5in) long and weighs 14gm (0.5oz). It is now obviously human and the rounded head is less tucked forward against the chest. Inner ears, eyes, and most main internal organs including the heart are now completely formed. Blood circulates around the foetal body. Limbs lengthen and now have wrists and ankles and well-defined fingers and toes.

Week 16 The foetus is 18cm (7in) long and weighs 113gm (4oz). The emphasis shifts from development to growth. Limbs have well-developed joints and muscles, hair appears, and the foetus is now obviously male or female.

Week 20 The foetus is 25cm (10in) long and weighs 340gm (12oz). Eyebrows, nails, and nipples form, and the foetus moves about inside the womb. Its heartbeat can be heard by stethoscope.

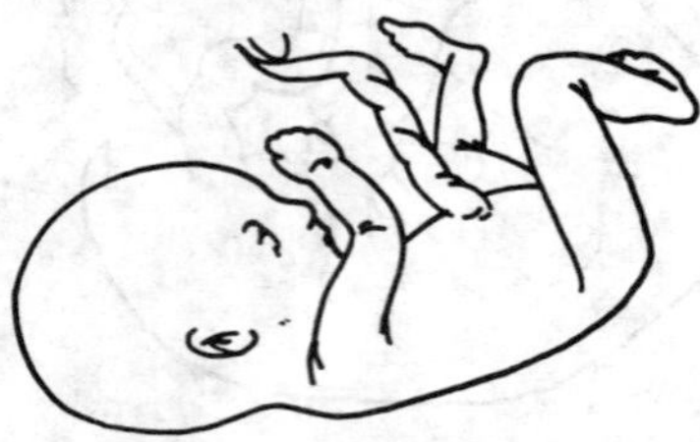

12 weeks

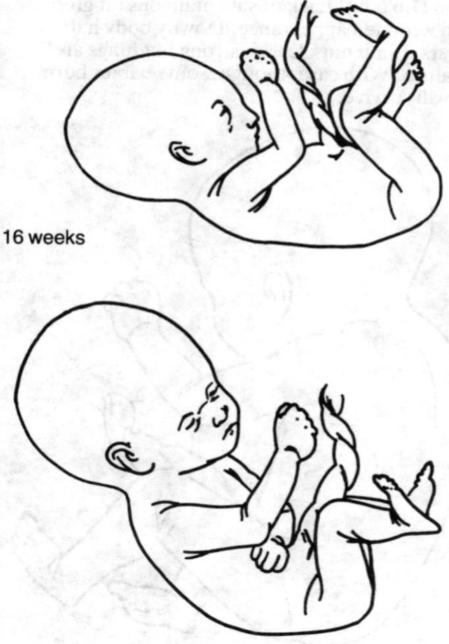

16 weeks

20 weeks

Week 24 The foetus is 33cm (13in) long and weighs 623gm (1lb 6oz). Lack of subcutaneous fat gives skin a wrinkled appearance. Downy body hair appears. Limb muscles are strong but lungs are immature. With care, though, some babies born now will survive.

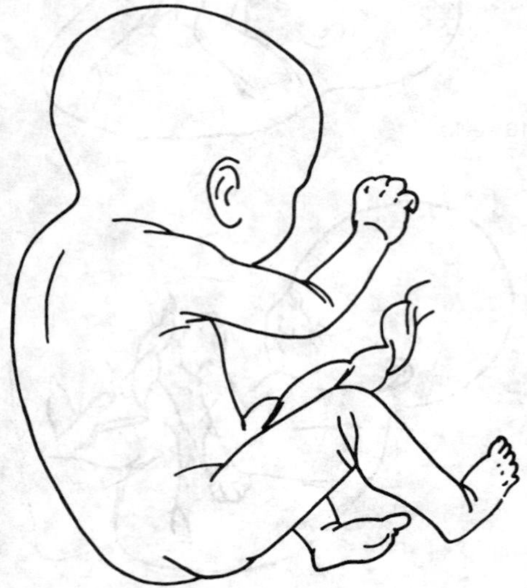

24 weeks

Week 26 The fast-growing foetus assumes body proportions close to a full-term newborn infant's.

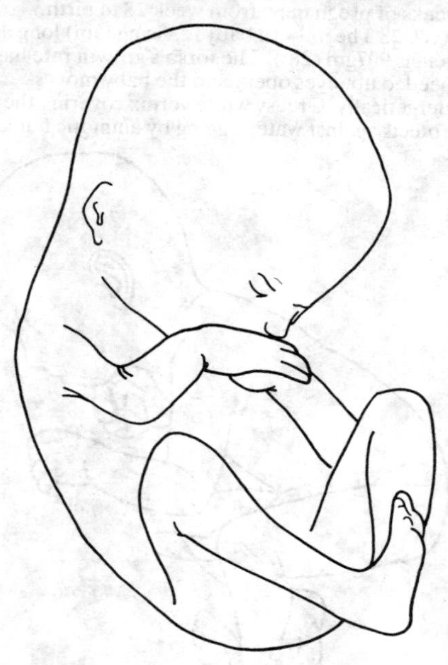

26 weeks

Weeks 28–40
Pictures show changes to a foetus through the last weeks of pregnancy: from week 28 to birth.
Week 28 The unborn baby is 38cm (15in) long and weighs 907gm (2lb). The torso's growth rate has speeded up, eyes open, and the baby moves energetically. Greasy white vernix covering the skin protects against waterlogging by amniotic fluid.

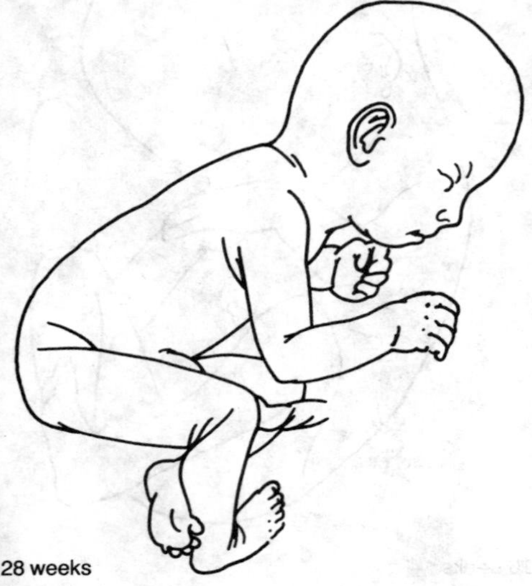
28 weeks

Week 32 The unborn baby is 43cm (17in) long and weighs 1.8kg (4lb). Head-body proportions approach a full-term baby's, and lungs are quite well developed. The baby turns upside down in the womb.

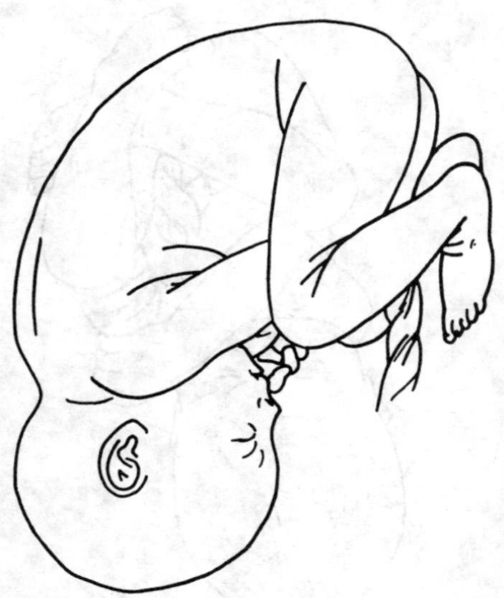

32 weeks

Week 36 The unborn baby is 46cm (18in) long and weighs 2.38kg (5lb 4oz). Fat deposition makes the body better rounded and the skin less wrinkled. Fingernails are growing, and (in boys) the testes may descend into the skin bag called the scrotum.

36 weeks

Week 40 At birth a typical baby is about 50.8cm (20in) long and weighs 3.18kg (7lb). It has smooth skin and a rounded body, and has usually lost its foetal growth of lanugo, the downy hair once covering a large part of the body. (Birth often happens up to two weeks before or after the predicted date, and newborn boys are often longer and heavier than newborn girls.)

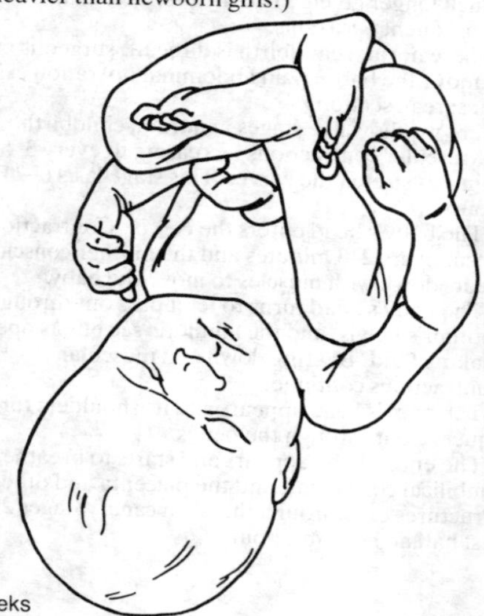

40 weeks

Childbirth

Normally childbirth follows labour: a mother's muscular contractions forcing her baby from the uterus out through the birth canal. The whole process lasts 6–25 hours. Usually a woman takes much longer giving birth the first time than on subsequent occasions.

Where normal childbirth is difficult, surgeons may remove the baby by an abdominal operation called caesarean section.

Here we show five stages in normal childbirth.

1 Muscular contractions increasing to every 3–5 minutes stretch the cervix. This stage lasts 6–24 hours.

2 The baby's head enters the cervix. Contractions occur every 2–3 minutes and the mother consciously bears down with muscles to move the baby.

3 The baby's head turns to let it pass out through the mother's pelvis, and the amniotic sac bursts open, leaking fluid. Bearing down and muscular contractions continue.

4 The baby's head appears and its shoulders turn to squeeze out through the pelvis.

5 The entire baby appears and starts to breathe. Its umbilical cord is cut, and the placenta and other structures exit through the birth canal. Stages 2–5 last half an hour to 1 hour.

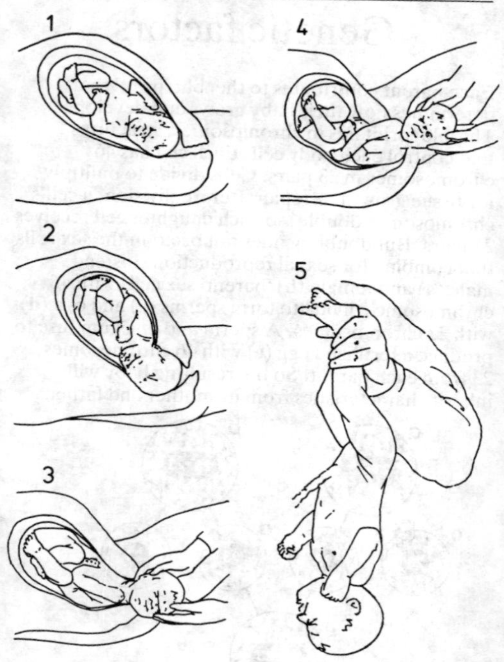
1
2
3
4
5

Genetic factors

Each parent contributes to the 'blueprint' that determines how their baby grows and develops. This blueprint lies in chromosomes, structures that control each body cell. Each cell has 46 chromosomes in 23 pairs. Cells divide to multiply for tissue growth or repair. Before division, a cell's chromosomes double, so each daughter cell receives 23 pairs. But doubling does not occur in the sex cells that combine for sexual reproduction. Instead, male (**a**) and female (**b**) 'parent' sex cells with 46 chromosomes divide to form sperms (**c**) and ova (**d**) with 23 chromosomes. A sperm and an ovum fuse to produce a fertilized egg (**e**) with 46 chromosomes, 23 from each parent. So the resulting baby will inherit characteristics from its mother and father.

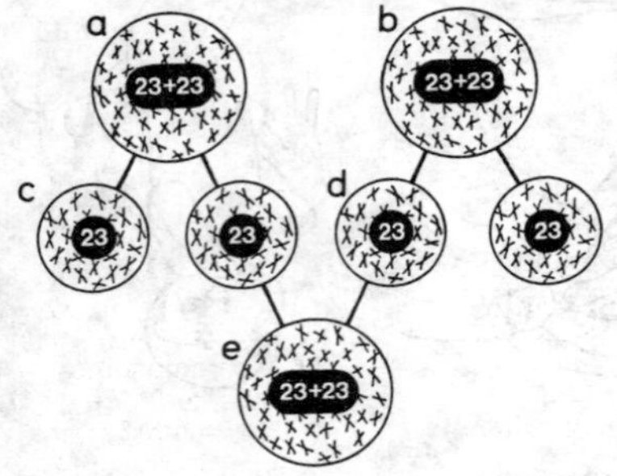

Male or female?
A baby's sex depends upon special chromosomes that it inherits. Each body cell in its mother included a pair of X-shaped sex chromosomes. Each body cell in its father included one X and one Y sex chromosome. A baby inherits only one sex chromosome from each parent. If the baby inherits two Xs it will be female. If it inherits one X and one Y it will be male. Here we show four ways by which a mother (**a**) and father (**b**) can hand on sex cells to produce a daughter (**c**) or a son (**d**).

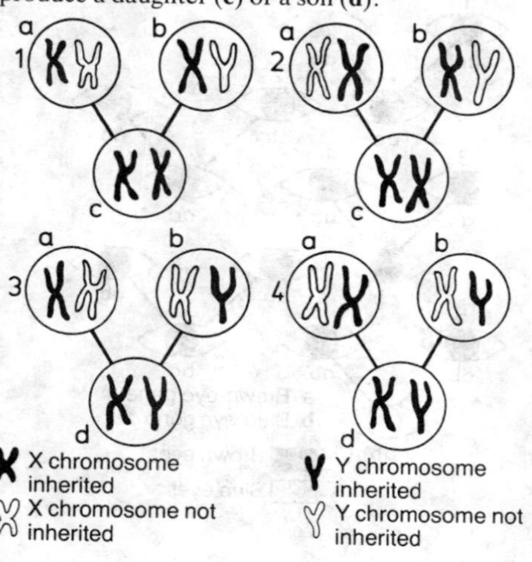

Inherited eye colours

From parents we inherit aspects of temperament and physical appearance. Such things as colour of the eyes and hair are coded for in genes: units borne on chromosomes. Each type of gene occurs in pairs, and each pair that we inherit contains one gene from each parent. In an inherited pair a dominant gene will 'overpower' a recessive gene. Diagrams show the gene for brown eyes (**a**) dominating the gene for blue eyes (**b**) in four of five examples.

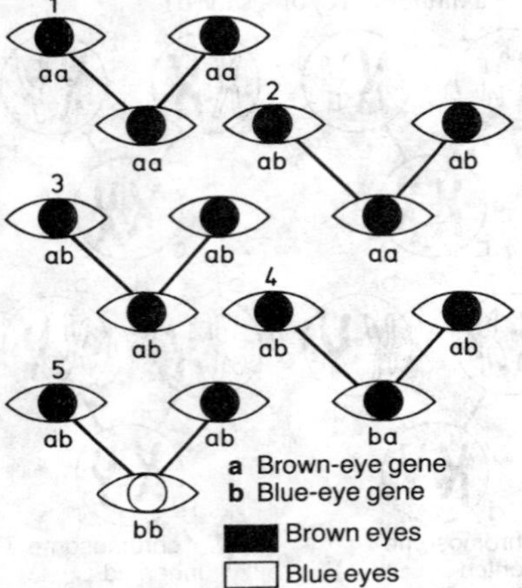

Inherited hair colour

Recessive genes can pass through several generations before they reappear, as with the gene that makes hair red. This is because the brown-hair gene dominates the red-hair gene. As these diagrams show, generations of two families of brown-haired people can unknowingly hand on a red-haired gene. Only when an individual inherits two of these recessive genes will that person have red hair. Thus in some ways some of us resemble our own parents less than we resemble our grandparents or even our great-grandparents.

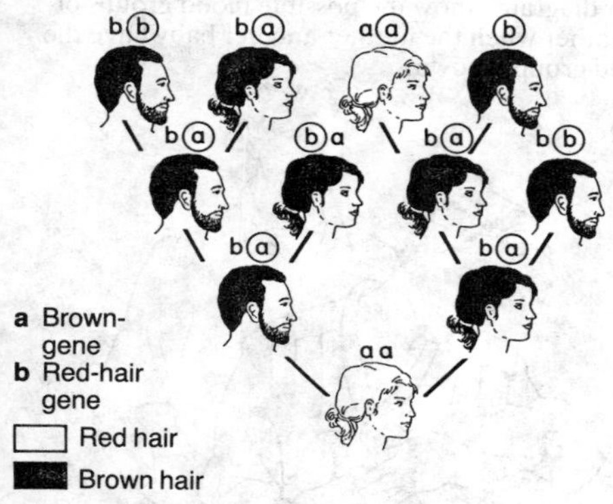

Gene handed on to the next generation

Inherited blood groups
Genetics (the science of heredity) reveals that people inherit various types of blood. Blood donors' and patients' blood groups are an important factor in blood transfusions, where compatibility is vital. Also, in paternity cases, a blood-group mismatch between a man and child helps to prove that the man could not have been the father of the child.
Presence or absence of two factors known as A and B give rise to four blood groups: A, B, AB, and O. A and B blood each contain one factor. AB blood has both factors. O has neither.
Four diagrams show the possible blood groups of the father when the mother and her baby have the blood groups shown.

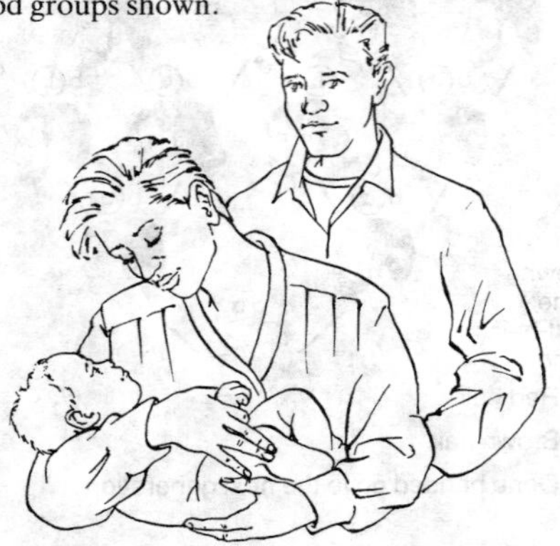

Table to show possible blood groups of father

	Baby's blood group			
	O	**A**	**AB**	**B**
Mother's blood group **O**	O, A, B	O, A, B		O, A, B
A	A, AB	O, A, AB, B	O, A, AB, B	A, B
AB		AB, B	A, AB, B	A, AB
B	AB, B	AB, B	O, A, AB, B	O, A, AB, B

Growing up

Body proportions change with changing growth rates of head, limbs, and trunk. One-quarter of total length at birth, the head is only one-eighth of total length by adulthood. Legs increase from

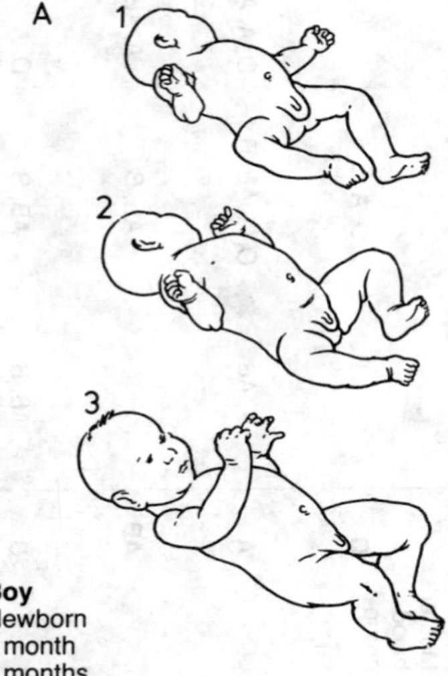

A Boy
1 Newborn
2 1 month
3 3 months

three-eighths to one-half total length. The trunk gets relatively slim.

Meanwhile bone, fat, and muscle grow at different rates. Thus plump, short-limbed, large-headed babies become relatively thin, wiry schoolchildren. These then become broader: girls especially at hips and boys at shoulders. Individual variations in physique can start appearing at the early age of two.

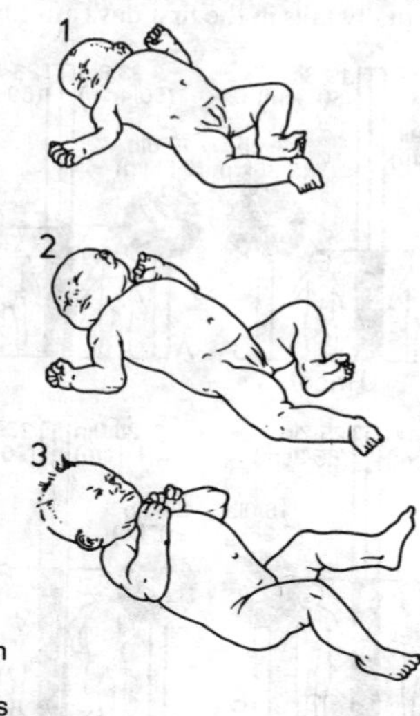

B Girl
1 Newborn
2 1 month
3 3 months

Growth, ages 0–3

A baby grows fastest in the three months just before its birth. Growth continues quickly in the first three years of life, but the rate of growth in length and weight is slowing down.

Growth in length is greatest in year one. A baby lengthens in its first three months by as much as in the 12 months between ages 2 and 3.

Weight actually falls in the first days after birth, but

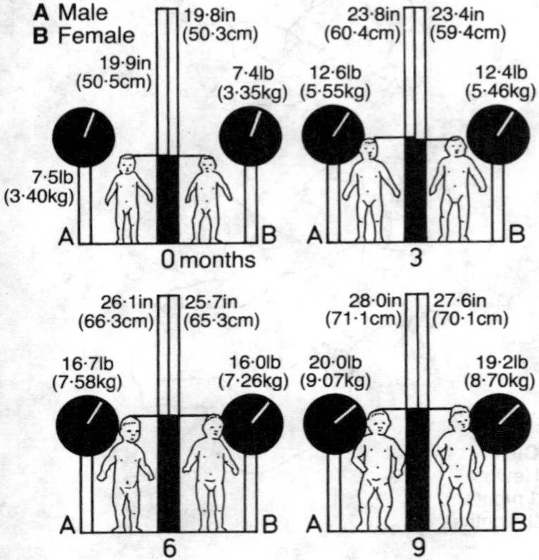

A Male
B Female

19·9in (50·5cm)
19·8in (50·3cm)
7·5lb (3·40kg)
7·4lb (3·35kg)
A B
0 months

23·8in (60·4cm)
23·4in (59·4cm)
12·6lb (5·55kg)
12·4lb (5·46kg)
A B
3

26·1in (66·3cm)
25·7in (65·3cm)
16·7lb (7·58kg)
16·0lb (7·26kg)
A B
6

28·0in (71·1cm)
27·6in (70·1cm)
20·0lb (9·07kg)
19·2lb (8·70kg)
A B
9

a large baby doubles its birthweight in the first six months while a much smaller baby's birthweight trebles. Weight gain halves in the second six months to a level equal to the whole gain for the second year. In the third year weight gain slows down even more.

Here, two sets of weights and heights contrast the gains in length and weight achieved by boys and girls between birth and the age of 3.

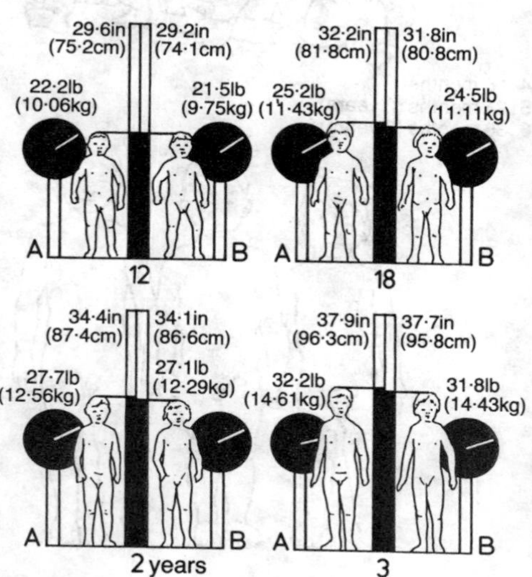

A Boy
1 6 months
2 9 months
3 12 months (1 year)

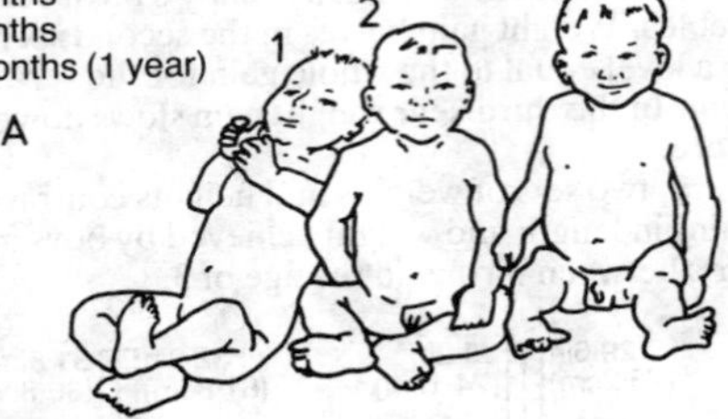

4 18 months
5 24 months (2 years)
6 36 months (3 years)

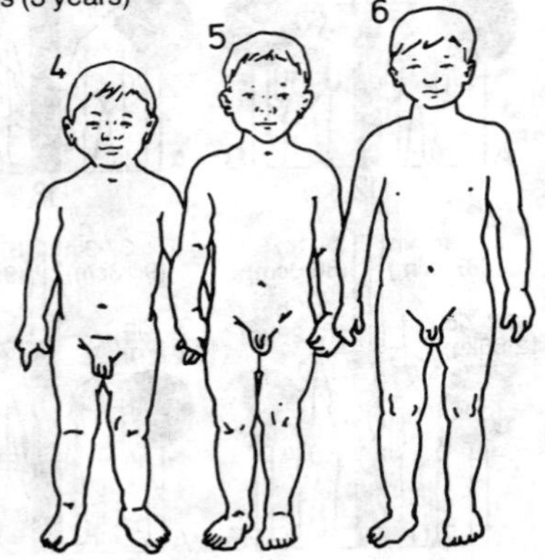

B Girl
1 6 months
2 9 months
3 12 months (1 year)

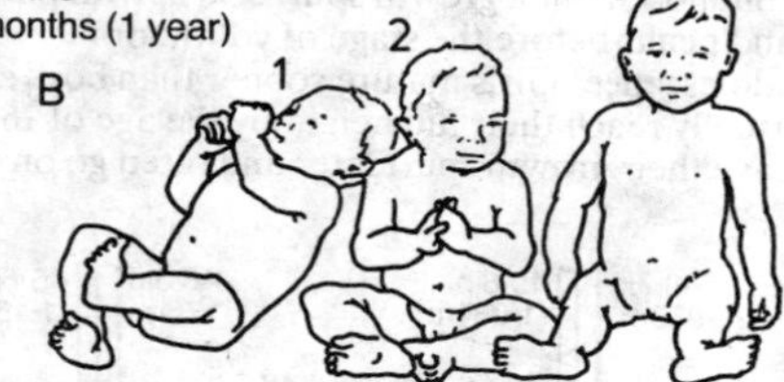

4 18 months
5 24 months (2 years)
6 36 months (3 years)

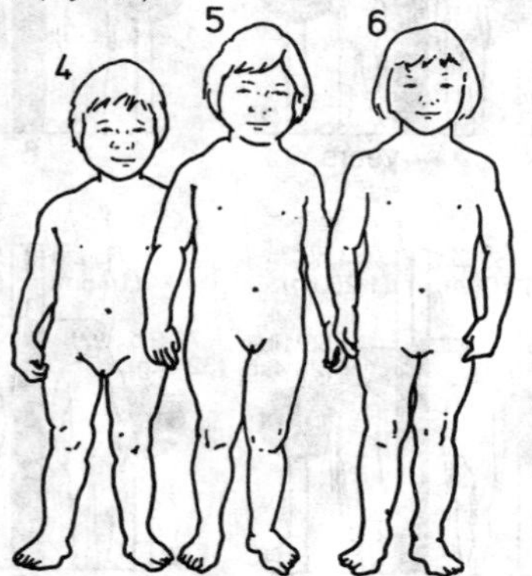

Growth, ages 4–18 years

Growth in length slows down during middle childhood, but a growth spurt sets in with puberty and peaks before the stage of youth, or adolescence. Girls mature sooner than boys and usually reach their full height by the age of 16. Boys have their growth spurt later and often go on

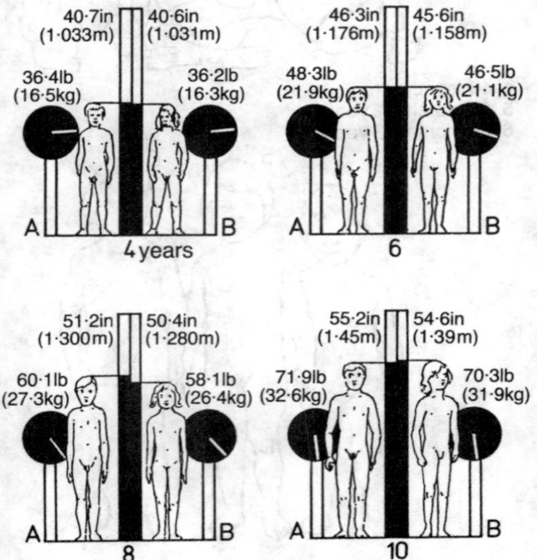

growing after 18.
Weight gain broadly matches growth in length. Girls put on the most weight between ages 10 and 14; boys between ages 12 and 16.
Here, two sets of weights and heights contrast the gains in length and weight achieved by boys and girls aged between 4 and 18.

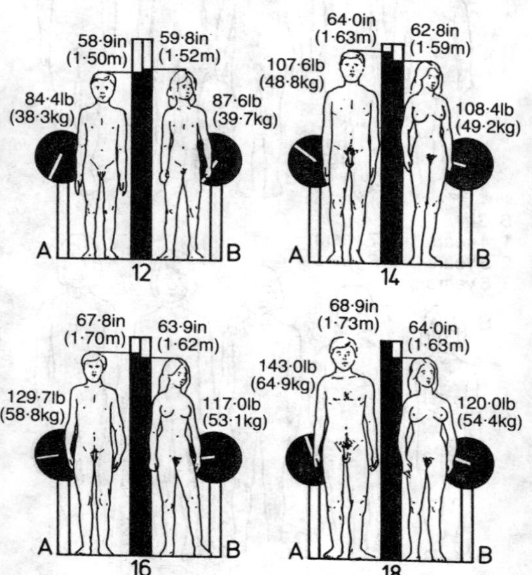

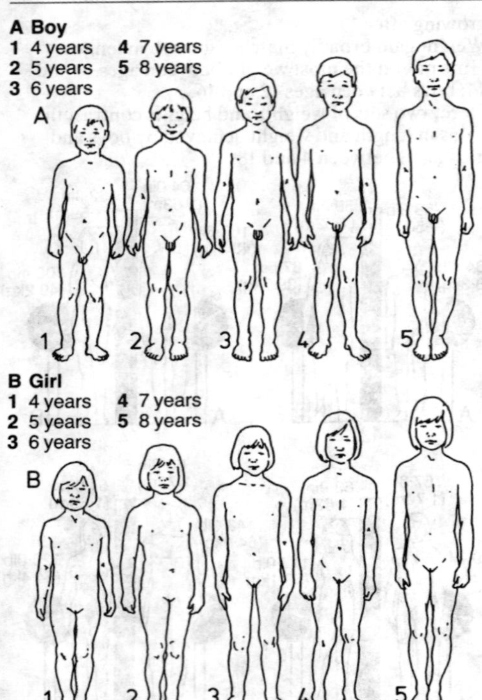
A Boy
1 4 years
2 5 years
3 6 years
4 7 years
5 8 years
A
1
2
3
4
5
B Girl
1 4 years
2 5 years
3 6 years
4 7 years
5 8 years
B
1
2
3
4
5

A Male
1 10 years **3** 14 years
2 12 years **4** 18 years

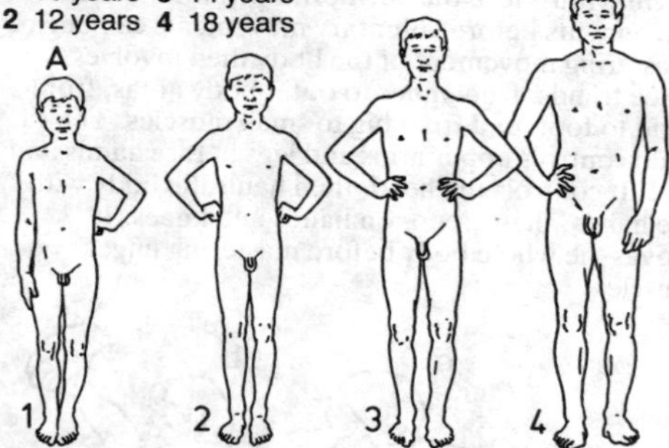

B Female
1 10 years **3** 14 years
2 11 years **4** 18 years

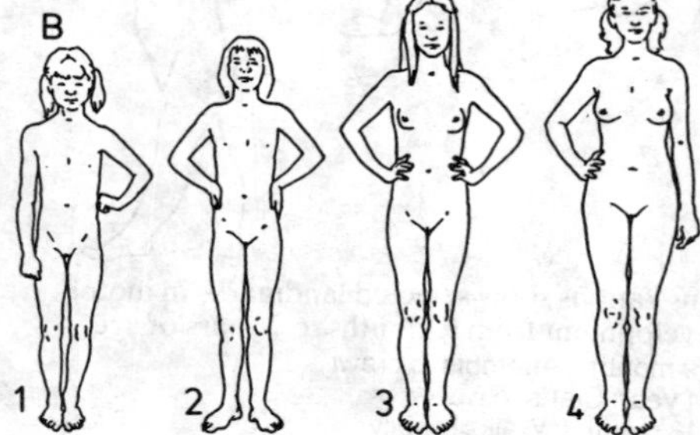

Motor development

A child must lose the newborn's primitive reflex movements before voluntary movements can begin. Mastering movement of the body then involves three trends: from inner to outer body areas, from head to foot, and from big to small muscles. Thus a child controls upper arms and legs before hands and feet. It controls the head, then hauls the body with the hands, then creeps on hands and knees. It moves the whole body before mastering finger muscles.

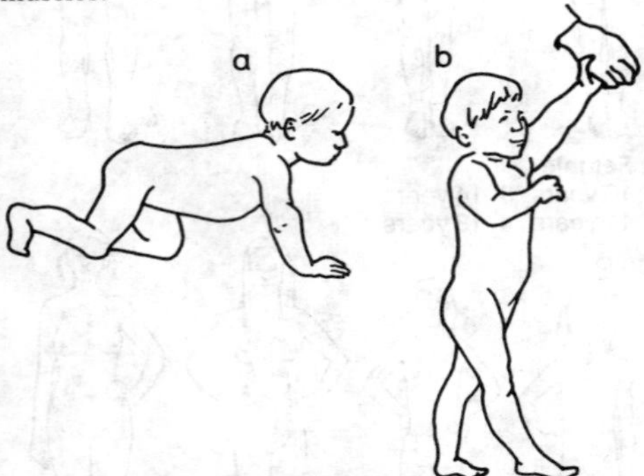

Illustrations show selected landmarks in motor development from 9 months to 7 years of age.

a 9 months: Attempts to crawl
b 1 year: Starts to walk
c 18 months: Walks readily

d 2 years: Runs readily
e 3 years: Kicks a ball hard
f 4 years: Hops on one foot
g 5 years: Walks along a narrow line
h 6 years: Jumps over a rope 25cm (10in) high
i 8 years: Rides a bicycle

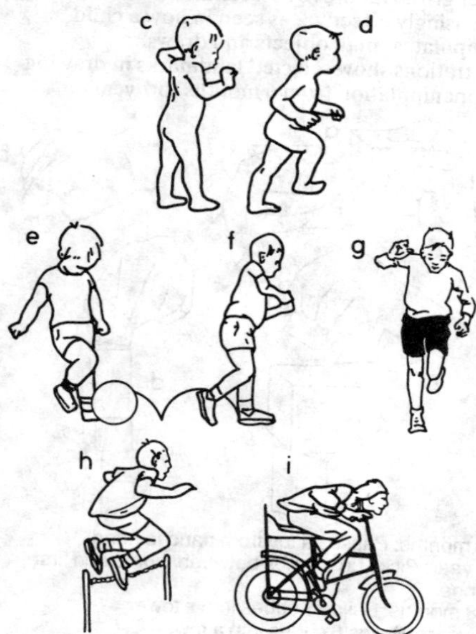

Hand and eye development

Tests indicate that babies have begun gaining colour vision by 3 months, are perceiving shape and size by 6 months, and have normal depth and field of vision by 1 year old. By then they also have a thumb-and-finger grip. Hand-eye co-ordination now become increasingly effective, as seen in how a child manipulates small objects and draws.

Illustrations show selected landmarks in drawing and manipulation from 6 months to 7 years.

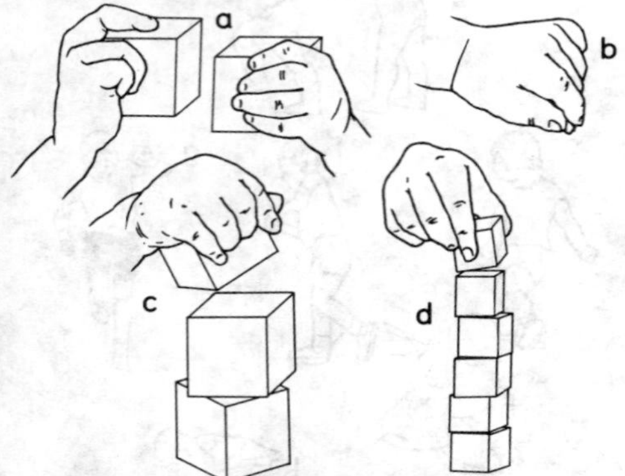

- **a** 6 months: Passes a toy from hand to hand
- **b** 1 year: Picks up crumbs between thumb and first finger
- **c** 18 months: Builds 3 cubes into a tower
- **d** 2 years: Builds 6 cubes into a tower

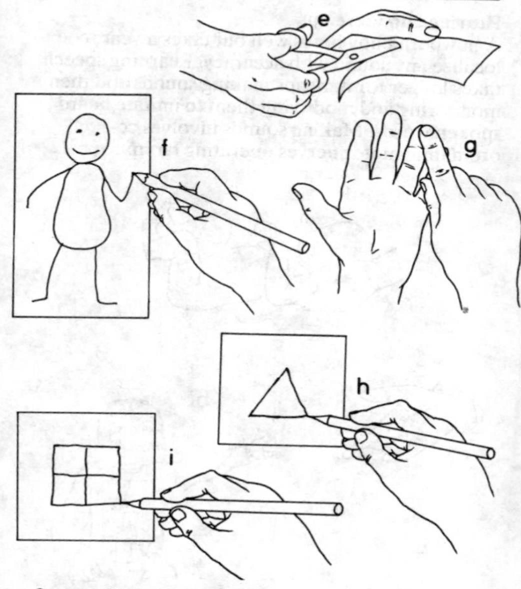

e 3 years: Uses scissors to cut paper
f 4 years: Draws a man with head and legs, and maybe trunk and arms
g 5 years: Counts the fingers of one hand
h 6 years: Draws a triangle quite well
i 7 years: Draws a window (a cross inside a square)

Hearing and voice

A newborn baby hears well but takes a year to localize any sound with accuracy. Learning speech takes longer for it means making sounds and then monitoring and modifying them to imitate heard spoken words. Making sounds involves co-ordinating motor nerves operating larynx, vocal

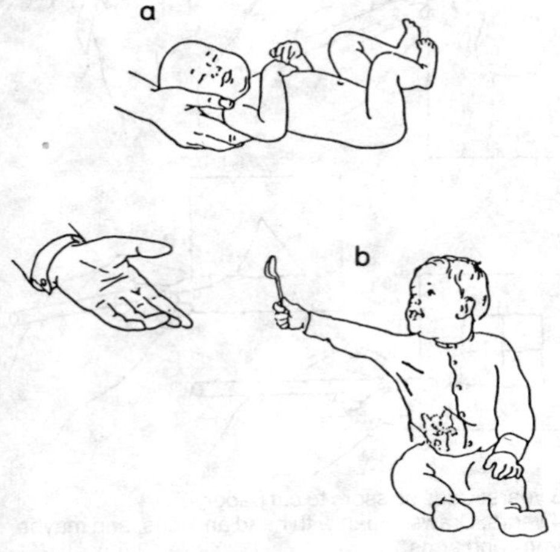

a 6 months: Chuckles and squeals playfully
b 1 year: Hands an adult an object when asked

cords, pharynx, soft palate, tongue, and lips. Monitoring speech involves feedback to the brain from speech muscles and the ears. Learning speech is difficult after the age of 3, so deaf children need help early on.

Illustrations show selected landmarks in hearing and voice from 6 months to seven years.

c 18 months: Says 6–20 words but knows many more
d 2 years: Enjoys listening to favourite stories.
e 3 years: When asked, starts assembling a doll's house.

f 4 years: Can say or sing some nursery rhymes
g 5 years: Enacts stories with friends
h 6 years: Can say how one object resembles a similar object
i 7 years: Says how 3 objects differ from a broadly similar object

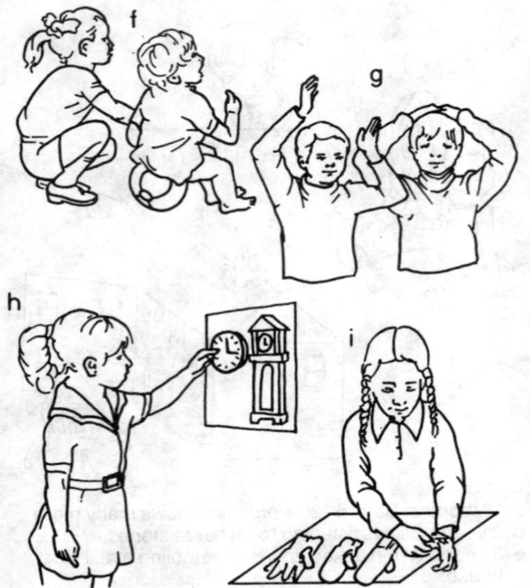

Mental development
Swiss psychologist Jean Piaget thought intellectual development passed through stages involving interacting cognitive and emotional factors.
1 Sensorimotor stage (0–2) Largely non-verbal. Children learn partly by handling objects but start symbolizing with words and gestures.
2 Pre-operational stage (2–7) Children manipulate words, and learn by experience, intuition, and trial and error. The pictured child might say that the tall narrow container (**a**) holds more water than the short broad container (**b**) although the child saw equal amounts of water poured into both.
3 Concrete-operational stage (7–12) Children begin classifying objects by difference and similarity.
4 Formal operations (12 onward) Children use thought to deal with hypothetical matters.

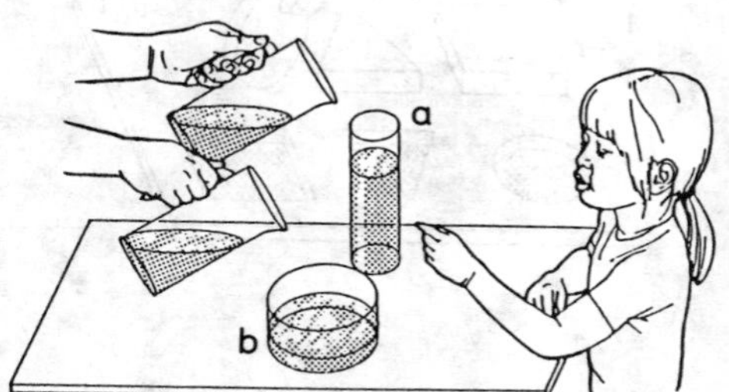

The learning process
Some psychologists reject the idea of cognition (or knowing) and think learning at any age is based on mental habits forged by a sequence of stimulus, response, and reward. Thus the stimulus of a puzzle makes a child respond by trying to solve it. The pleasure of solving the puzzle is the reward. The child mentally links effort with reward, so solves the puzzle faster next time around. However, insight

also improves with age, as these pictures suggest.
1 At 2 years a child tries fitting a block into a hole in a formboard puzzle without taking account of the shapes of the block and the hole.
2 At 2½ years the child tries another hole if the block does not fit in the first hole tried.
3 At 3 years the child mentally matches blocks and holes before fitting the blocks in the holes.

Male puberty
Puberty is the process that turns a child into a sexually mature adult. Illustrations show typical developments that change a boy into a man. This often lasts from 12 to 18. The sex hormone testosterone helps create mature male sex organs producing sperms. Male hormones also produce secondary sexual characteristics: a tall, muscular

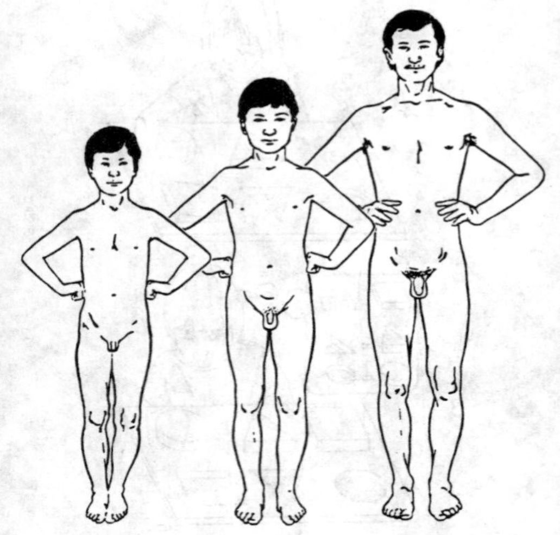

physique, beard, chest hair, and deepened voice. Before puberty boys have a small scrotum and penis and no body hair. Early puberty produces growth in testes, penis, pubic hair, and height. Later puberty (ages 15–18) enlarges penis and prostate gland, produces facial and body hair, deepens voice, adds height and weight, and broadens shoulders.

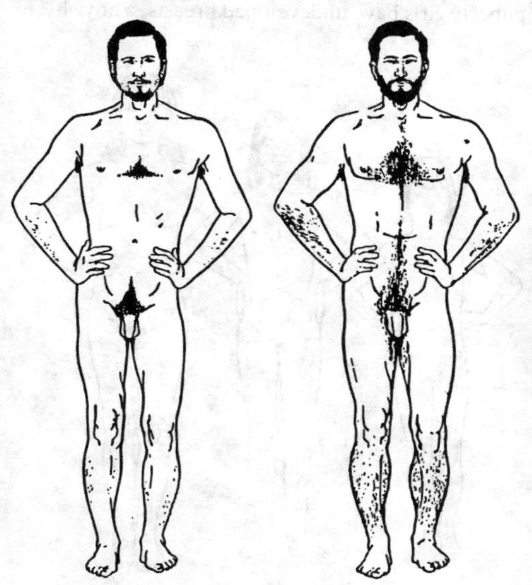

Female puberty
Illustrations show typical developments that change a girl into a woman. In girls this can take from 11 to 17. The sex hormone oestrogen helps create mature female sex organs and eggs. Female hormones also produce secondary sexual characteristics: breasts, broad hips, and rounded body contours. Before puberty girls have undeveloped breasts, a boyish

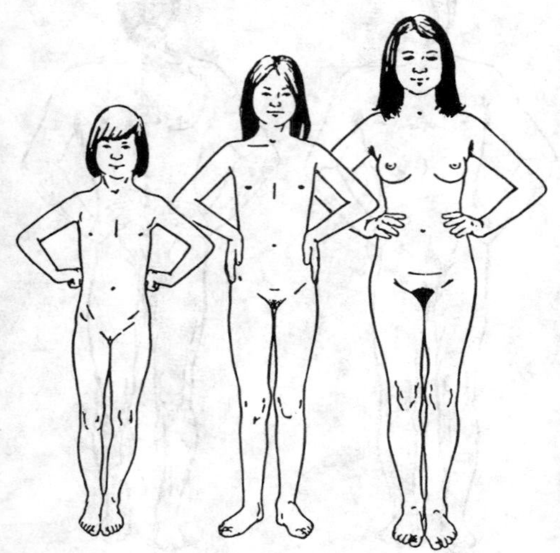

shape, and no body hair. Early puberty thickens vaginal walls; produces pubic hair and menstruation; develops breasts; broadens the pelvis; adds fat to hips; and increases height. Later puberty (14–17) sees genitals mature, pubic hair thicken, rounding of body shape, and an end to growth in height. Breast development, and weight gain extend into the early 20s.

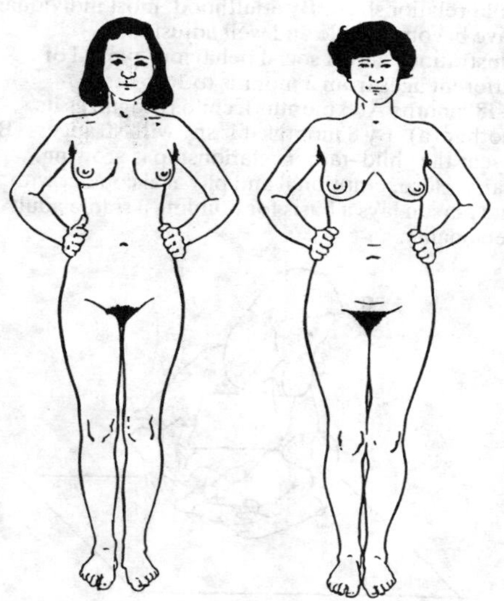

Social development
As they grow older, children experience swings of behaviour from well balanced, lively, and outgoing to unstable, withdrawn, and moody. But early and affectionate parental care promotes healthy long-term social development. First imitating, and then rebelling against parents, many children eventually grow up to build secure husband–wife and parent–child relationships. By adulthood, most individuals have become stable and well adjusted.
Illustrations depict social behaviour typical of different ages from 3 months to 16 years.
0–18 months At 3 months a child recognizes its mother (**a**). By 8 months it is shy with strangers. By 1 year the child–father relationship is growing. Early, close, emotional and physical contact with one person lays a basis for building a stable adult personality.

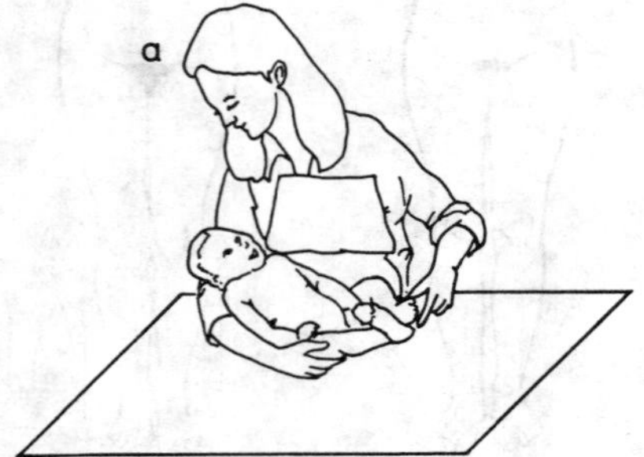

18 months–5 years Early on children identify with and imitate their parents (**b**). Most parents discourage overdependence and aggressive outbursts. By 2 children cannot play with others, but by 3 they are old enough for the give and take of games.

5–12 years Most children have a best friend by the age of 5 (**c**), but group games become increasingly important, and children begin questioning formerly accepted parental values.

Adolescence Fast growth and sexual development confuse young teenagers. Conforming to their age group's behaviour and fashions helps give a reassuring sense of identity. By 16 most adolescents begin heterosexual activity (**d**) and relationship with parents may start becoming more mature.

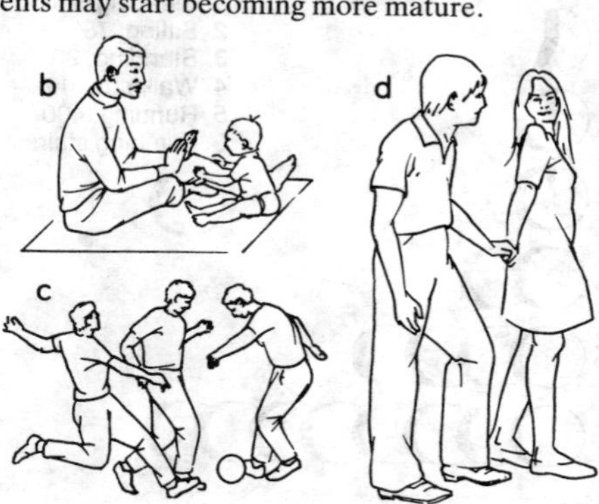

The food we need

We need to eat to stay alive. Foods give our bodies energy and heat, and substances for body growth, maintenance, and repair. Scientists measure food energy in calories. Our need for these depends on age, sex, and level of activity. Here we show (opposite) numbers of calories required per day by 'typical' males and females in temperate climates.

Food and exercise

We show the number of calories per hour used by a woman performing different activities. (A man's calorie requirements would be greater.)

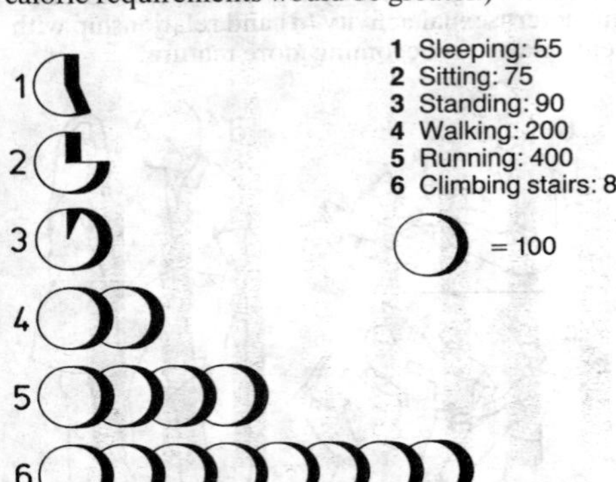

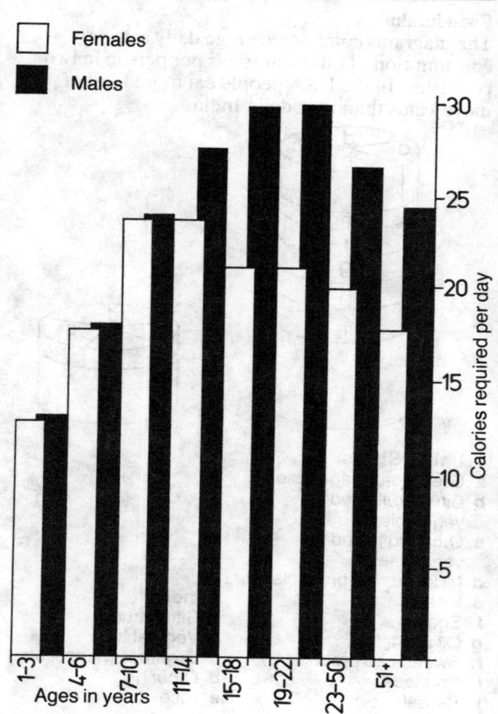
Females
Males
30
25
20
15
10
5
Calories required per day
1-3
4-6
7-10
11-14
15-18
19-22
23-50
51+
Ages in years

Food intake

The diagrams compare average daily calorie consumption of different foods per person in two countries. In the USA people eat more food of more kinds than they do in India.

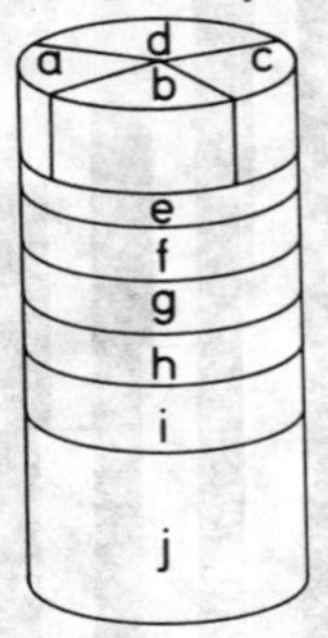

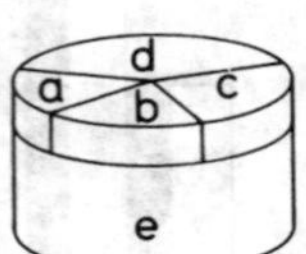

1 United States

- **a** Green leafy vegetables
- **b** Citrus fruits and vegetables
- **c** Other fruits and vegetables
- **d** Milk and milk products
- **e** Meat
- **f** Eggs
- **g** Oil and fat
- **h** Sweetened products
- **i** Potatoes
- **j** Cereals

2 India

- **a** Citrus fruits
- **b** Vegetables
- **c** Legumes (beans, etc.)
- **d** Other
- **e** Rice

Nutrients in food

Foods give us proteins, carbohydrates, fats, vitamins and minerals.

1 Proteins build and repair body cells. Meat, fish, eggs, milk, beans, grains, and nuts are rich in proteins.

2 Carbohydrates provide energy for rapid use. They include sugars in fruits, sugar cane, and sugar beet; and starches in potatoes, cereals and other vegetables.

3 Fats are concentrated stores of energy, found in butter, margarines, edible oils, meat, eggs, etc.

4 Vitamins in tiny quantities help regulate chemical processes inside the body. Different vitamins occur in fats and oils, fresh fruits and vegetables, and other substances.

5 Minerals of certain kinds abound in milk, cheese, fish, and some green vegetables.

Healthy eating

Many nutritionists consider that a healthy daily diet is based on foods from each of four main groups (helpings shown are those for adults).

A Milk and cheese 2 or more cups of milk
B Fruit and vegetables 4 or more servings
C Meat and pulses (beans, etc) 2 or more servings
D Bread and cereals 4 or more servings

(People with certain medical problems need special diets. Avoiders of animal fats must make sure they still get enough Vitamin D. Vegans [vegetarians avoiding all animal products] must take special care that their diet includes vital amino acids.)

Input and output

For a man weighing 70kg (154lb) here is the daily input of food, water, and other substances the body needs, balanced by its output of body wastes. (Water is not a food but it transports substances around the body and accounts for two-thirds of body weight. Solid foods as well as liquids contain water.)

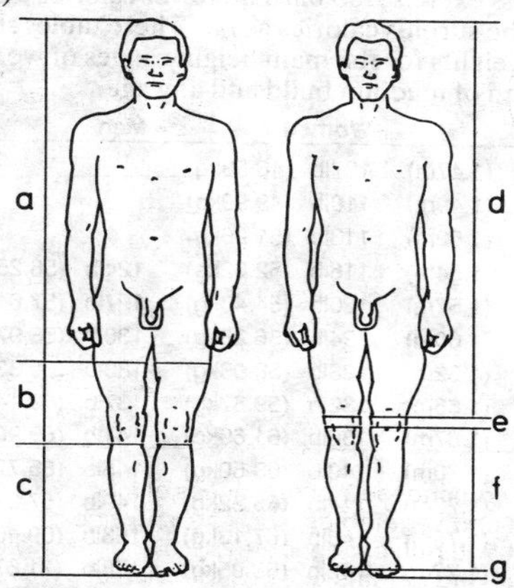

Input 3500gm (7.7lb)

a Water 61.3%
b Food 14.6%
c Oxygen 24.1%

Output 3500gm (7.7lb)

d Water 70.9%
e Solids 1.7%
f Carbon dioxide 25.9%
g Others 1.5%

Ideal weights

People eating no more than their bodies need have an ideal weight that varies with their sex and height. Weight often increases in middle age, largely because people eat the same amount as before but take less exercise, so burn up fewer calories and store the surplus calories as fat. These tables show ideal weights for the main height ranges of women and men of medium build and any age.

Height		Women		Men	
4ft 10in	(1.47m)	107lb	(48.53kg)		
4ft 11in	(1.49m)	110lb	(49.90kg)		
5ft 0in	(1.52m)	113lb	(51.26kg)		
5ft 1in	(1.54m)	116lb	(52.62kg)	124lb	(56.25kg)
5ft 2in	(1.57m)	120lb	(54.43kg)	127lb	(57.61kg)
5ft 3in	(1.60m)	124lb	(56.25kg)	130lb	(58.97kg)
5ft 4in	(1.62m)	128lb	(58.06kg)	133lb	(60.33kg)
5ft 5in	(1.65m)	132lb	(59.87kg)	137lb	(62.14kg)
5ft 6in	(1.67m)	136lb	(61.69kg)	141lb	(63.96kg)
5ft 7in	(1.70m)	140lb	(63.50kg)	145lb	(65.77kg)
5ft 8in	(1.72m)	144lb	(65.32kg)	149lb	(67.59kg)
5ft 9in	(1.75m)	148lb	(67.13kg)	153lb	(69.40kg)
5ft 10in	(1.77m)	152lb	(68.95kg)	158lb	(71.67kg)
5ft 11in	(1.80m)	157lb	(71.21kg)	162lb	(73.48kg)
6ft 0in	(1.83m)			167lb	(75.75kg)
6ft 1in	(1.85m)			171lb	(77.56kg)
6ft 2in	(1.88m)			176lb	(79.83kg)
6ft 3in	(1.90m)			181lb	(82.10kg)

Personal hygiene

Washing helps to keep the body clean, sweet smelling, and free from some disease bacteria.

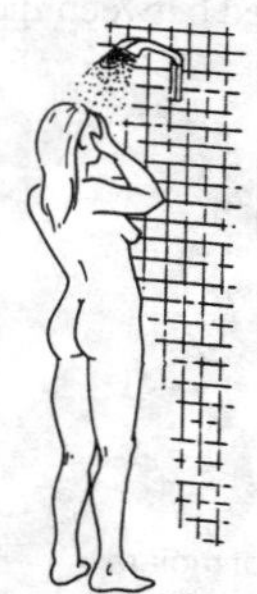

1 Washing hands with soap and water before meals and after visiting the lavatory helps prevent the spread of germs that might cause serious diseases of the digestive system.

2 Washing armpits , genitals , and feet helps prevent the spread of germs responsible for body odour.

3 A daily bath or shower rids skin of dirt, salt from dried sweat, flakes of old, dead skin, and bacteria that might cause skin infections.

4 Regularly washing hair with soap and water or a mild shampoo removes dirt and the flakes of dead skin known as dandruff.

Cleaning teeth

Cleaning teeth removes food and plaque, a soft creamy deposit formed by sweet foods and indirectly causing tooth and gum decay. Toothbrushes clean the surfaces of teeth; dental floss or toothpicks remove food lodged between the teeth.

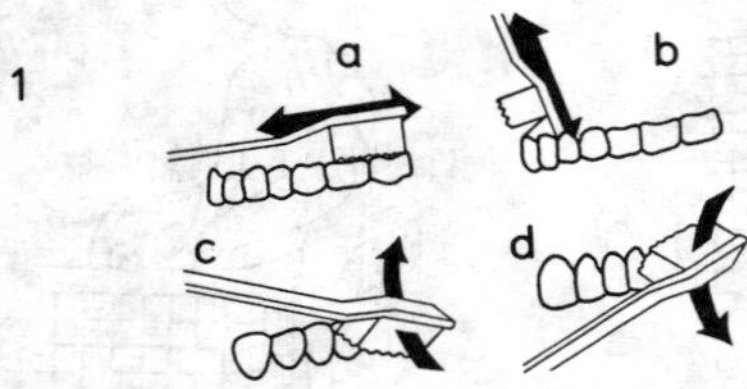

1 Using a toothbrush correctly
- **a** Brushing back and forth across tops of molars
- **b** Brushing the backs of front teeth up and down
- **c** Brushing bottom side teeth upwards with the brush held sideways
- **d** Brushing top side teeth with a downwards action

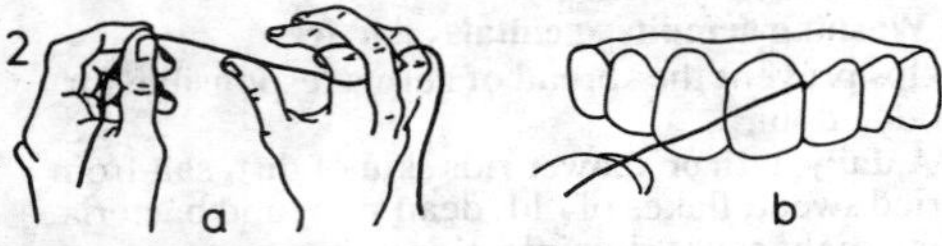

2 Using dental floss
- **a** Break off a piece of fibre about 5cm (2in) long
- **b** With a sawing action, guide the fibre between teeth, dislodging food and plaque

Posture and exercise

Standing with a good posture (**1**) involves vertically aligning the centres of gravity of different sections of the body (**a–g**). Good posture balances the muscles around each joint and helps to keep the body stable and resilient.
Standing with a bad posture (**2**) means the centres of gravity of some body sections fall outside the body's main centre of gravity in the pelvis (hip girdle). Bad posture commonly occurs with sedentary work and lack of exercise. The consequence is often muscle strain, a common cause of backache.

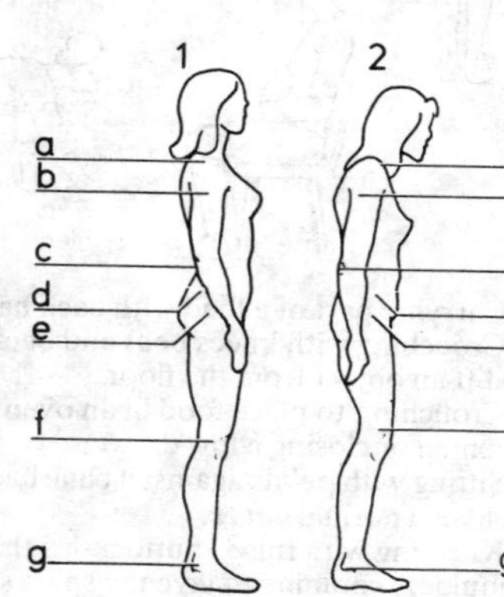

a Neck
b Shoulders
c Lower back
d Pelvis
e Hip joints
f Knee joints
g Ankle joints

Good posture

Keeping a good posture involves remembering to keep the body's centres of gravity in balance, whatever activity you may be doing.

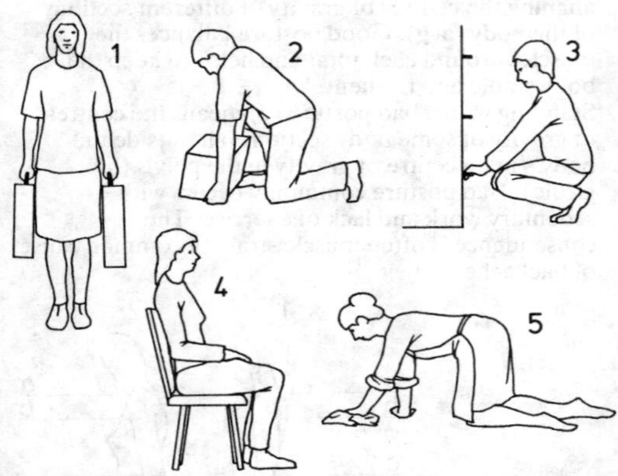

1 Carrying part of a load with each hand.
2 Crouching with knees bent and back held upright to lift an object from the floor.
3 Crouching to place food in an oven or when opening or closing a low drawer.
4 Sitting with pelvis against a chairback and spine held in a normal curve.
5 Kneeling with raised buttocks so that hips and shoulders combine to give the spine support.

Fitness
The fitter your body the more efficiently it works. Fit individuals complete their daily tasks and still have energy to spare.
Fitness involves five factors (others include agility, balance, co-ordination, and speed).

1 Body composition: Fat content, proportions, shape, and weight/size ratio (partly inherited, partly determined by diet and exercise).
2 Flexibility: Range of joint movements.
3 Strength: The force contracting muscles can apply to move a load (the rate at which muscles move a load is muscle power).
4 Muscular endurance: How long specific muscles can perform a task before fatigue sets in.
5 CR (cardio-vascular and respiratory) fitness: The ability of heart and lungs to supply oxygen to muscles and remove waste products. CR fitness arguably matters more than all the rest.

The fit heart

Exercise makes the heart and lungs work harder to meet the muscles' needs for extra blood and oxygen.

Bar diagrams contrast the performance of an unfit heart (**1**) and a fit heart (**2**). Bar lengths show relative numbers of heartbeats per minute. Bar subdivisions show a heart's work at rest (**a**), its reserve capacity (**b**), and its potential reserve capacity (**c**). At rest an unfit heart has only a small reserve capacity, so beats much faster during exercise. After exercise an unfit heart takes a long time to slow down to normal.

A heart made fit by regular exercise grows stronger, bigger, and more efficient. A fit heart pumps more blood with every stroke, so it beats more slowly than an unfit heart. It also has a large reserve capacity, and after exercise soon slows to normal.

Pulse rates

Bar lengths contrast the resting pulse rates typical of three kinds of athlete and an unfit person with a sedentary occupation.

1 Sprinter: 66 beats per minute
2 Distance runner: 45 beats per minute
3 Marathon runner: 40 beats per minute
4 Sedentary individual: 84 beats per minute

Testing CR fitness

Healthy people aged 10–69 can check their comparative CR (circulatory-respiratory) fitness by stepping on and off an 20cm (8in) bench or step. Test stepping involves four operations.

a Place the left foot on the step.
b Bring the right foot up beside the left foot.
c Move the left foot back and down.
d Move the right foot back and down.

Repeat this 24 times a minute for 3 minutes. Wait a minute then take your pulse. Count the beats for 30 seconds. Multiply by two. Then check your rating:

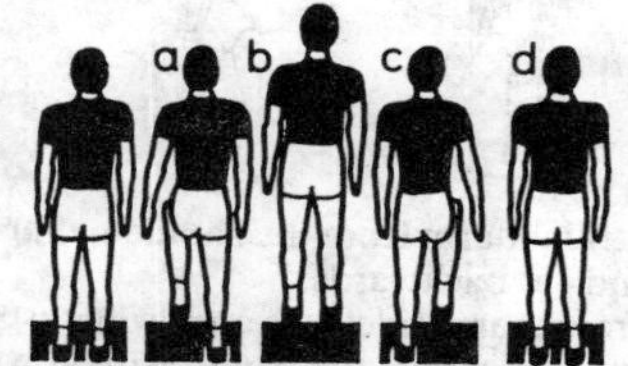

Performance	Men	Women
Excellent	–68	–76
Good	68–79	76–85
About average	80–89	86–94
Below average	90–99	95–109
Very poor	100+	110+

Testing flexibility
Disuse restricts joint flexibility at any age. Reasonably fit individuals can test shoulder, elbow, hip, and neck flexibility against that of the pictured figure; arrows indicate average range of movement. (Other tests apply to other joints.)

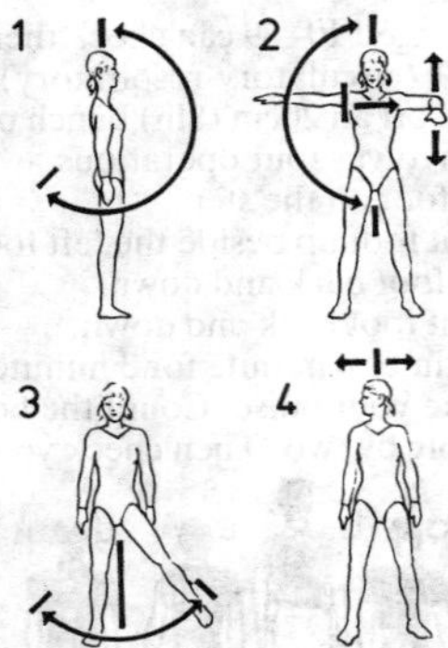

1 Swing a straight arm from the shoulder 180° forwards and 45° backwards.
2 Hold a straight arm sideways and swing it 180° up and down and 40° across the front. With arm held sideways and elbow bent, swing forearm straight up and down.
3 Swing a straight leg 45° to the side and 40° across the front.
4 Turn the head 90° to each side.

Testing strength
Six exercises test the strength of the main muscle groups. To perform them at all needs only low-level fitness. Repetition may be much harder. But practice brings improvement.

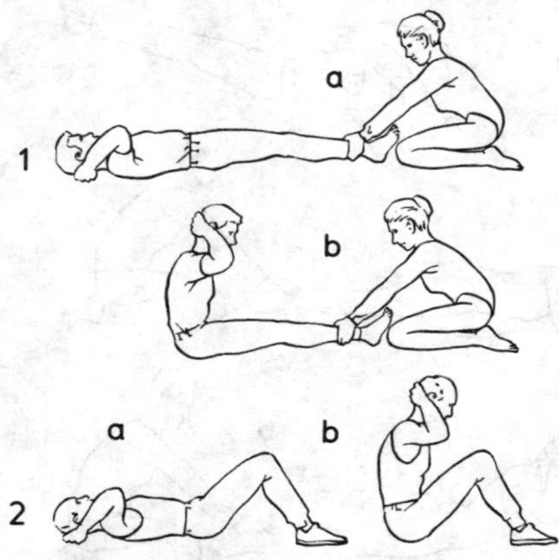

1 Abdominal and psoas (spine-thigh linking) muscles
a Lie on your back, hands behind head and feet held by a friend or under a low bar.
b With relaxed back, roll up to sit.
2 Abdominal muscles
a Lie on your back with bent knees, feet on floor.
b Hands behind head, roll to sit.

3 Psoas and lower abdomen
a Lie on your back with legs straight.
b Feet together, lift heels 25cm (10in) and keep them up for 10 seconds.

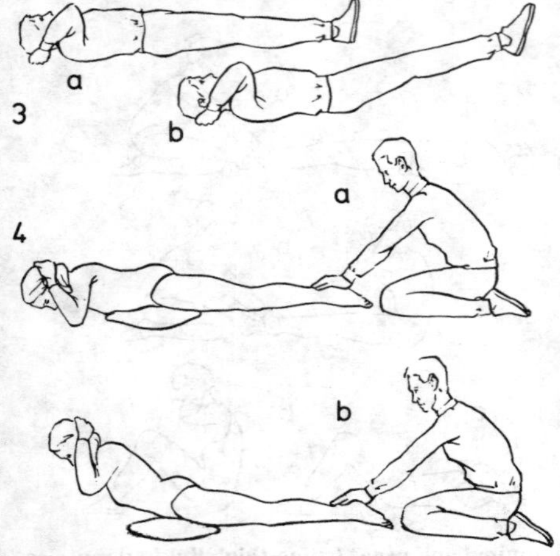

4 Upper back muscles
a Lie face down, hands behind head, with a pillow supporting hips and abdomen, and someone holding your feet down.
b Lift head, shoulders, and chest and keep them off the ground for 10 seconds.

5 Lower back muscles
a Lie as in **4a** but with arms below face and someone holding your chest down.
b Keeping legs and feet straight, lift them and hold off the ground for 10 seconds.

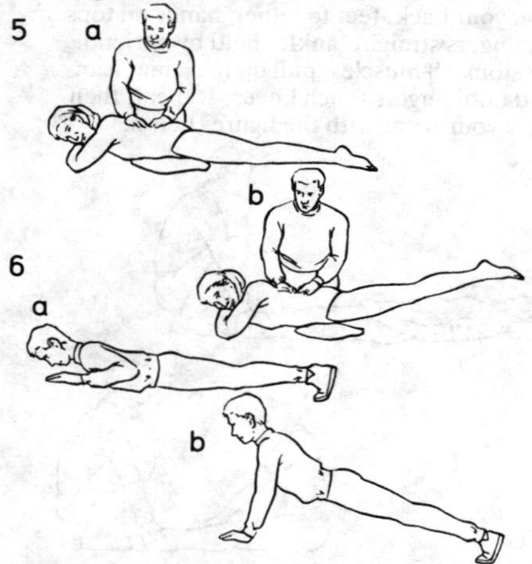

6 Chest, shoulders, triceps
a Lie face down, with hands palms down and fingers forward under shoulders, and toes tucked forward.
b Holding legs and body in a straight line, press down with your hands and straighten your elbows, lifting your body clear of the ground.

Muscular endurance
Muscular endurance is a muscle's ability to act for some time without fatigue. Sit-ups, squat thrusts, and push-ups test the endurance of various muscles.
1 Sit-ups
a Lie on your back, feet together, hands on tops of thighs, fingers straight, ankles held by a friend.
b With stomach muscles, pull up to sit and lean forward until fingers touch knees. Repeat, then compare your score with the figures below.

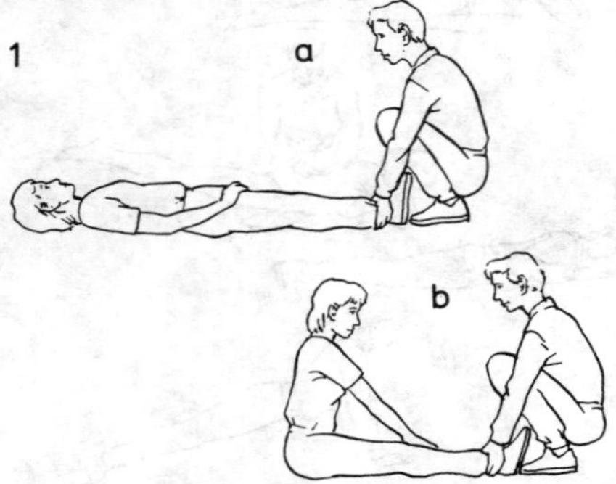

Score	Men	Women
Excellent	75+	35
Very good	50	25
Good	30	15
Average	20	10
Poor	10	5

2 Squat thrusts

a Stand erect and still.

b Bending knees and leaning forward, squat with palms on the ground.

c Supported on straight arms, thrust legs back to assume the pictured position. Go back to squatting, then standing. Try to repeat 10 times nonstop.

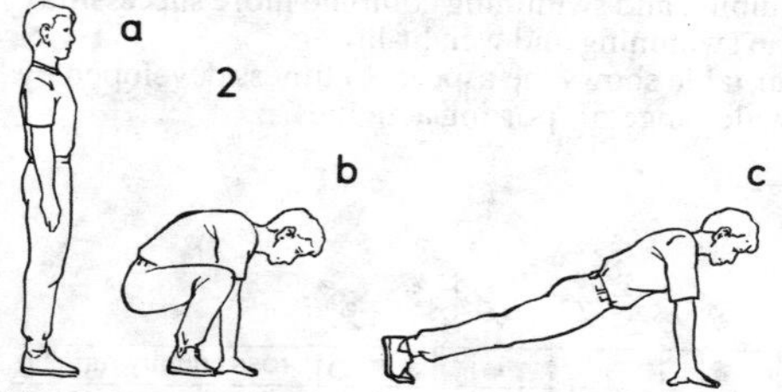

3 Push-ups

a Lying face down with straight legs, toes tucked forward, and hands palm down under shoulders.

b Push up by straightening elbows, holding body and legs in a straight line. Lower and repeat as many times as you can. (You will improve with practice.)

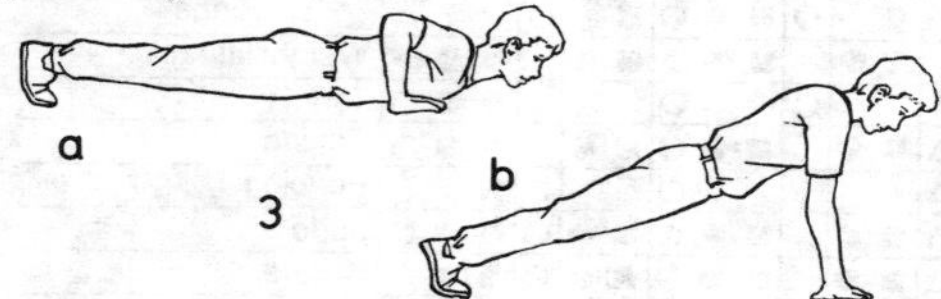

Sport and fitness

Some sports are better than others for developing different aspects of fitness. Subject to age and general health, enjoying several sports is a good way for most people to improve overall fitness and to build more than one group of muscles. Not all sports complement one another equally well. Running and swimming combine more successfully than swimming and weight-lifting.

Our table shows the aspects of fitness developed by a wide range of sporting activities.

	Back	Shoulders	Arms	Abdomen	Hips	Legs	
△	●			●		■ ● ○	Cross country running
△	■ ●	○	■ ● ○	■ ●	○	■ ● ○	Swimming
△	●		■ ●	●		■ ●	Water skiing
	■		○	■	○	■ ○	Gymnastics: Beam
	■	○	■ ● ○	■	○	■ ○	Floor exercises
	■		■ ● ○	■	○		Horse
	■	○	■ ● ○	■			Horizontal bars
	■	○	■ ○	■	○	○	Parallel bars
	■	○	■ ● ○	■	○		Rings
	■ ●		■ ●	■ ●		■ ●	Weight lifting
△		○	○			■ ● ○	Tennis
△	■ ●		■ ● ○	■ ●		■ ● ○	Boxing
△			○		○	■ ○	Fencing
△	■ ●		■ ● ○	■ ●	○	■ ● ○	Judo
△	■ ●		■ ● ○	■ ●	○	■ ● ○	Karate

△ **CR** (cardio-vascular and respiratory endurance)
■ Muscular strength
● Muscular endurance
▲ Flexibility

	Back	Shoulders	Arms	Abdomen	Hips	Legs	
△			○			■ ● ○	Tug-of-War
△	■ ●	○	■ ● ○	■ ●	○	■ ● ○	Wrestling
		○	○			○	Baseball
△						■ ● ○	Basketball
		○	○			○	Cricket
△	●		○		○	■ ● ○	Field Hockey
△		○	■ ● ○			■ ● ○	Lacrosse
△	■ ●		■	■	○	■ ●	Football: tackle
△	●				○	■ ● ○	Playground
△	■		■	■	○	■ ●	Ice Hockey
△			■			■ ● ○	Rugby
△						■ ● ○	Soccer
△						■ ● ○	Speedball
△		○	■ ● ○			■ ●	Volley Ball
△		○	■ ●			●	Water Polo

Sleep

Sleep is rest in which we become unaware of our surroundings, muscles relax, and breathing and heartbeat slow down. Sleep helps to revitalize the nervous system. Without sleep, people soon lose energy and concentration and grow irritable.
In orthodox sleep (75% of total sleep) the body is relaxed. During paradoxical sleep (25% of total sleep) dreams occur.

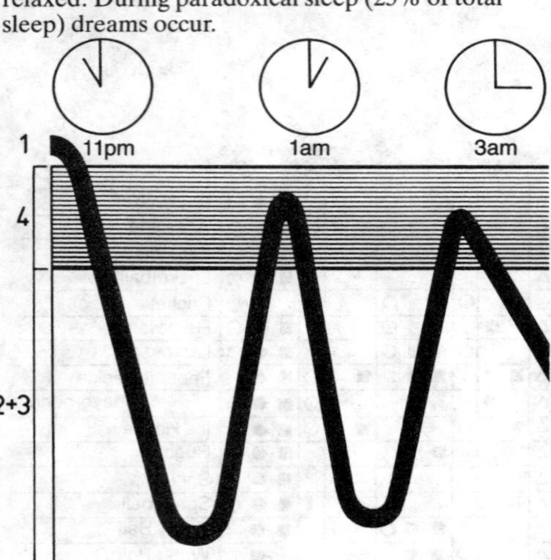

1 Consciousness We are aware of our surroundings.
2 Shallow orthodox sleep We are unaware of our surroundings.
3 Deep orthodox sleep Body building and repair processes reach their peak.
4 Paradoxical or REM (rapid eye movement) **sleep** Breathing and heartbeat grow irregular, eyes move to and fro between shut lids, brain activity increases, and we dream. There are three to five REM phases in eight hours' sleep.

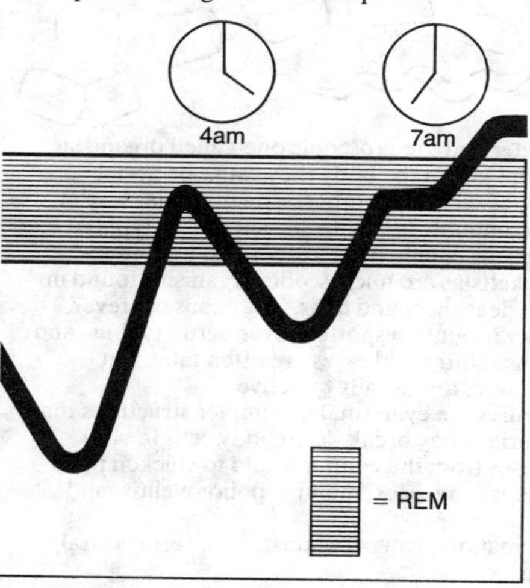

Infectious agents

Many diseases occur when tiny organisms infect the body, interfering with body processes or organs. We show much magnified examples from the six main groups of infective agents.

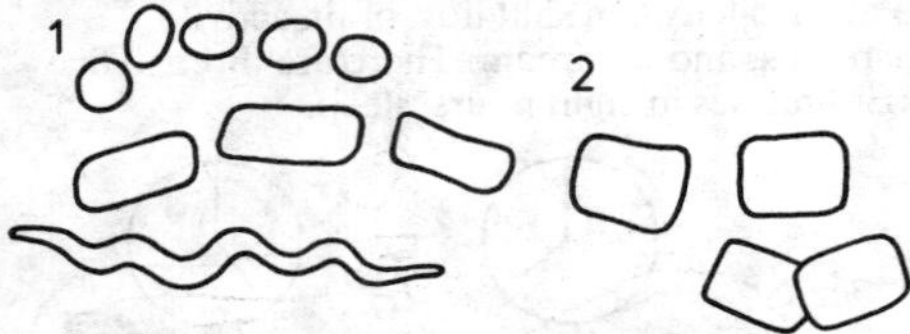

1 Bacteria are microscopic one-celled organisms. Multiplying in the body they cause bacterial diseases such as diphtheria, pneumonia, scarlet fever, tetanus, tonsillitis, tuberculosis, typhoid, and whooping cough. Most respond to antibiotics.

2 Rickettsias are microscopic organisms found in some fleas, lice, and ticks. They cause Q fever, Rocky Mountain spotted fever, scrub typhus, and typhus. Untreated cases are often fatal, but antibiotics are usually effective.

3 Viruses are even smaller, simpler structures than bacteria. They break down body cells in viral diseases from the common cold to chicken pox, influenza, measles, mumps, poliomyelitis, and AIDS.

Vaccination protects against some serious viral diseases.

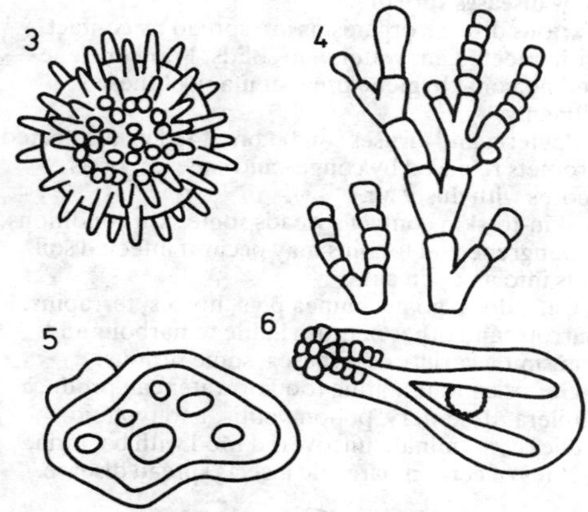

4 Fungi are non-green plant-like organisms. Some minute fungi cause athlete's foot, ringworm and certain lung diseases. Treatments include fungicides.

5 Protozoan parasites are one-celled 'animals' invading the body to produce diseases such as amoebic dysentery, malaria, and sleeping sickness.

6 Metazoan parasites are (many-celled) animals that live and feed on or in the body, causing irritation or disease. External parasites include fleas, lice, and ticks. Internal parasites include roundworms and tapeworms. Most common parasites can be eradicated.

How diseases spread

Various disease organisms are spread by contact with infected air, water, and solids. Food hygiene and personal hygiene prevent many of these ailments.

a Bacteria and viruses can be breathed in as infected droplets released by coughs and sneezes, or as spores with dusty air.

b Skin-to-skin contact spreads some skin conditions.

c Gangrene and tetanus may occur if infected soil gets into an open cut.

d Cats, dogs, goats, guinea pigs, horses, terrapins, parrots, and other pets are liable to harbour and transmit a variety of diseases, some serious.

e Germs contaminating food or water can produce cholera, dysentery, poliomyelitis, and typhoid.

f Flies contaminate uncovered food with bacteria.

g Bites of certain parasitic insects spread disease.

Tumours

Tumours are abnormal swellings produced when cells divide and multiply out of control. They can occur in almost any body system. Benign tumours (eg warts) grow slowly, may stop growing, and are usually harmless. Malignant tumours (cancers) spread fatally through body tissues unless soon killed by chemotherapy or radiation, or removed by surgery.

Four cross-sections contrast the growth of normal and malignant body cells.

1 Normal body tissue
2 Injured body tissue
3 Normal cell replacement
4 Malignant tumour in normal tissue
5 Malignant tumour invading nearby tissue

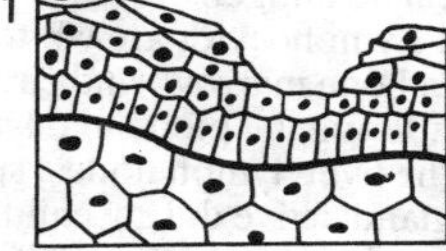

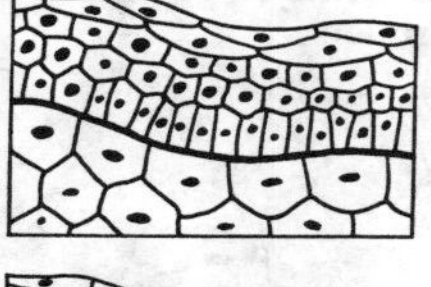

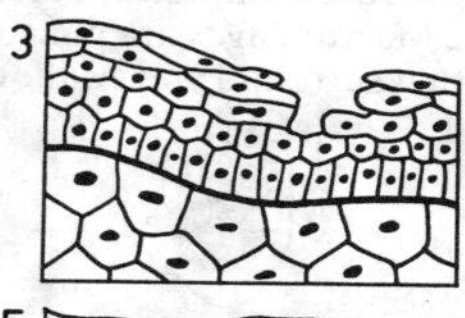

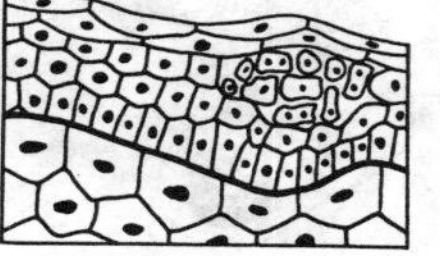

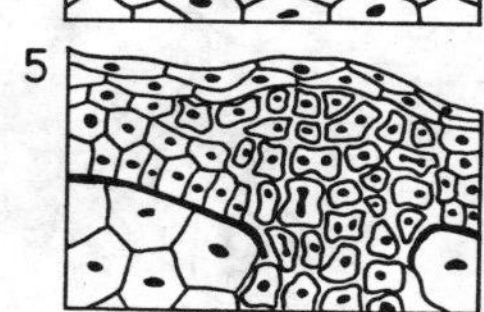

Body defences

The body has a succession of defences against invading germs and poisons.
First, skin and mucous membranes (eg of tonsils in the mouth) line body openings and produce various germicides. Few germs get through these barriers or survive the stomach's hydrochloric acid.
The body's main internal defences are white blood cells engulfing germs or producing antibodies: substances attacking harmful agents, collectively called antigens.
1 Lymphocytes are white blood cells manufactured in bone marrow, and circulating through and filtering the blood and lymph from concentrations in the liver, lymph nodes, spleen, and thymus (a chest gland active during childhood). Some lymphocytes produce antibodies, others control antibody output.
2 Macrophages are phagocytes: white blood cells that surround and swallow intruders.

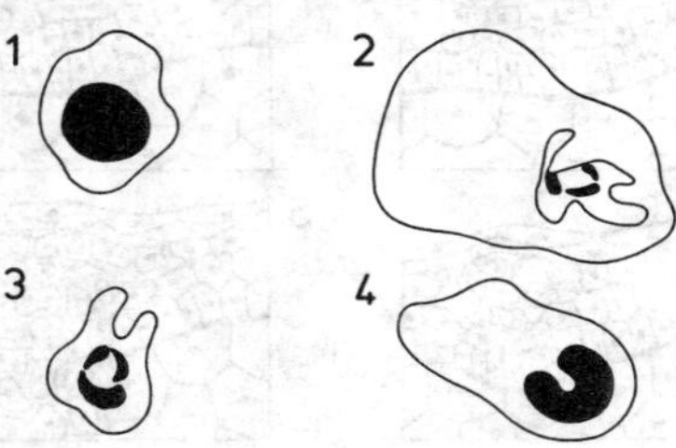

3 Neutrophils are also phagocytes.
4 Monocytes are a third type of phagocyte.
5 Antibodies (not shown) are circulating proteins that help to neutralize intruders. They interlock with the protein sheaths of bacteria or viruses. Then defensive proteins called complement coat the intruders, and phagocytes devour them. Each kind of antibody attacks just one kind of antigen. New kinds of antigen stimulate lymphocytes to produce new kinds of antibodies that confer immunity against a fresh disease, perhaps for life.
Because antibodies attack any foreign substance, special drugs are needed to prevent the body from rejecting transplanted organs.

Phagocyte in action
Three diagrams show a phagocytic cell (**a**) attacking and absorbing a bacterium (**b**).

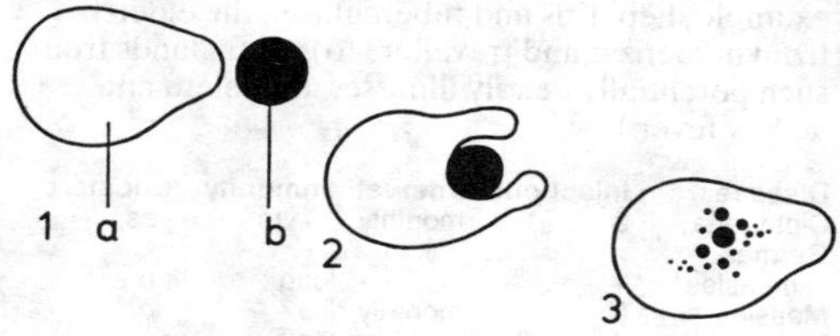

1 Phagocyte and bacterium
2 Phagocyte engulfing bacterium
3 Bacterium disintegrating inside phagocyte

Immunization

This is giving vaccines or serums to protect the body against specific diseases.

Active immunization (vaccination) is giving a vaccine that stimulates the body to produce its own antibodies, conferring maybe lifelong immunity against a disease.

Passive immunization is giving a serum containing ready-made antibodies that confer immediate but short-lived immunity.

Immunization against a disease involves one or more doses (usually injections). Diphtheria, whooping cough, and tetanus may be combined in one injection. Different vaccines involve different vaccination programmes, as indicated in the table for seven illnesses below (some vaccines may need fewer injections). Doctors recommend vaccinating children against these seven. (Other vaccinations help to protect high-risk groups against, for example, hepatitis and tuberculosis; the elderly from influenza; and travellers to certain lands from such potentially deadly illnesses as cholera and yellow fever.)

Disease	Injections	Interval	Immunity	Boosters
Diphtheria	3	monthly	10 yrs	yes
German measles	1		long	no
Measles	3	monthly	life?	no
Mumps	2	weekly	life?	no
Poliomyelitis	3 (oral)	monthly	life?	no
Tetanus	3	monthly	variable	yes
Whooping cough	3	monthly	10 years	yes

How cuts heal
Four diagrams show how healing closes a cut that has penetrated the skin's epidermis (**a**) and dermis (**b**).
1 Cut freshly made. Blood vessels (**c**) contract to stop blood leaking out and bacteria entering the body. Meanwhile clotting substances produce thread-like structures that begin to plug the cut.
2 First day. White blood cells (**d**) destroy foreign particles in the healing wound, and epidermal cells start multiplying from each side of the cut.
3 Second day. A scab (**e**) seals off the wound. Below the scab, epidermal cells growing in from both sides of the cut meet to form new epidermis.
4 After a week. The scab has fallen off to expose an area of new unbroken skin.

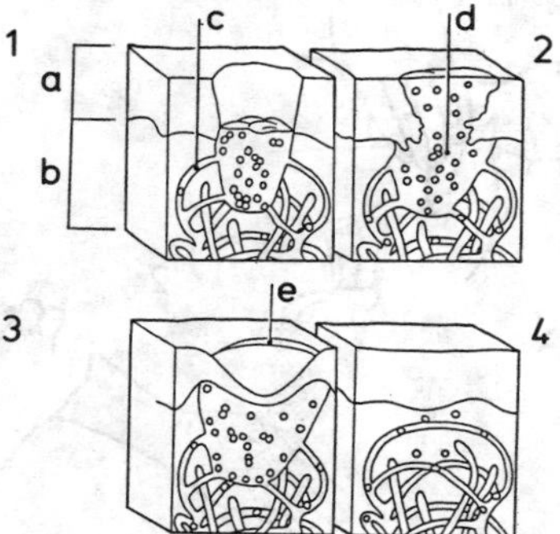

Minor first aid

We show two simple treatments for bleeding cuts and minor burns.

1 If a wound will not stop bleeding press a folded clean cloth on the wound. Add more cloths on top if bleeding persists. Hold still the affected part of the body. Bleeding from a badly cut but unbroken limb diminishes if you keep the limb above the rest of the body.

2 Run cold tap water over a small, superficial burn for several minutes. With clean hands gently wash and dry the burn if dirty. You could apply a soothing ointment. But if blistering occurs, cover with a sterile (not fluffy) dressing and bandage.

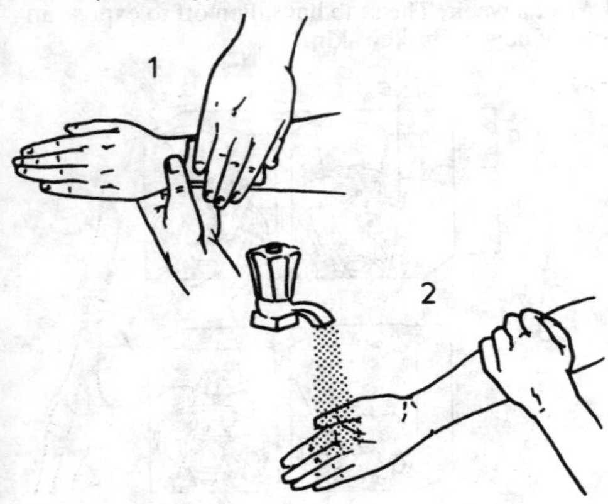

Bones and joints

Broken bones

Fractures are breaks in bones, especially brittle bones, a common feature of old age.

We show four common types of fracture:

1 Greenstick (incomplete break).
2 Simple (clean break with unbroken skin).
3 Compound (broken bone and skin).
4 Comminuted (shattered bone).

Fractures produce pain, swelling, and maybe grating sounds. X-rays reveal fractures. Treatment involves immobilizing the limb to allow the broken bone to regrow. Pinning bones is sometimes necessary.

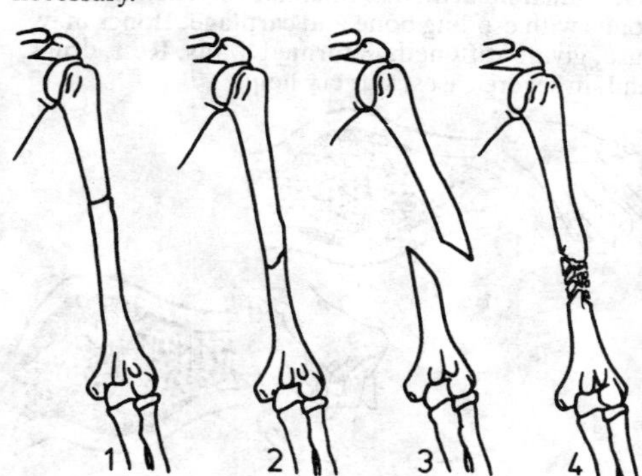

Problems with joints
Joints suffer various problems caused by injury or disease. Sprains are ligament injuries, usually needing only support by a bandage. Strains are muscle or tendon injuries. A slipped disc is bulging of a cartilage disc between two vertebrae. Dislocations are injuries separating the bones of a joint. Realignment sometimes means surgery. Rheumatism is any disorder producing pain in joints, notably two common problems.
1 Osteoarthrosis. Disintegrating cartilage with pain and stiffness, often in knees or hips, especially in older people. Careful exercise and reduced stress on affected joints help. Severe cases may require surgery.
2 Rheumatoid arthritis. Inflamed, swollen, painful joints with eroding bone and cartilage. Bones may fuse, giving stiffened, deformed joints. Rest, drugs, and, in severe cases, surgery help.

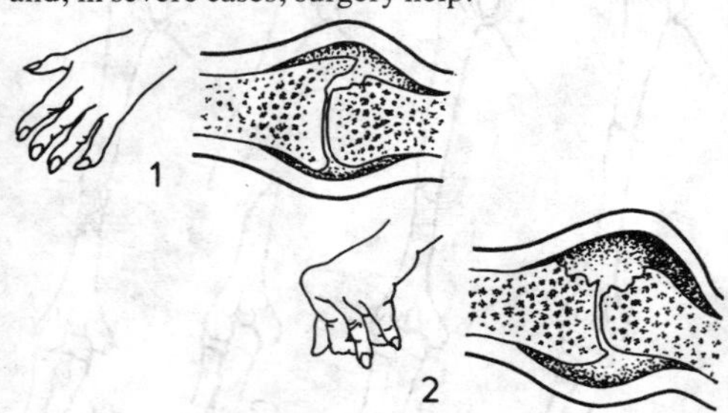

Headaches

Headaches can be due to injuries, infections, brain tumours, or nervous stress. All may affect pain-sensitive nerve endings in the head. Most headaches soon go or respond to painkilling drugs, but persistent headaches need medical attention. Here we show sources of a variety of pains in the head.

1 Nasal sinuses affected by respiratory infections or allergies.

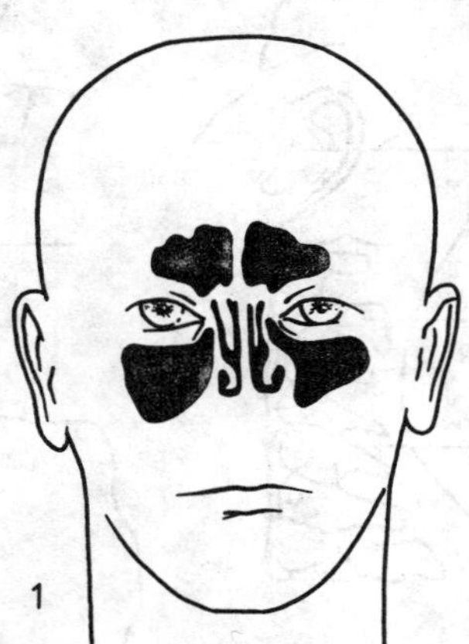

2 External sources include infected or injured ears (**a**), eyes (**b**), nose (**c**), teeth (**d**), or spine (**e**); also muscular tension in the neck (**f**), scalp (**g**), and face (**h**) and dilation of the temporal artery (**i**), a condition connected with the one-sided headache called migraine.

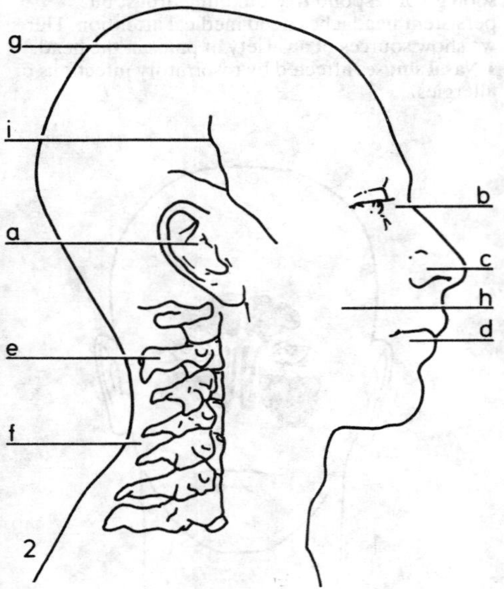

3 Internal sources of head pains include pressure or inflammation affecting veins **(j)** on the brain's surface, or cerebral arteries **(k)**, or parts of the dura mater **(l)**, a tough membrane surrounding the brain; or pressure or irritation affecting the trigeminal nerve **(m)**.

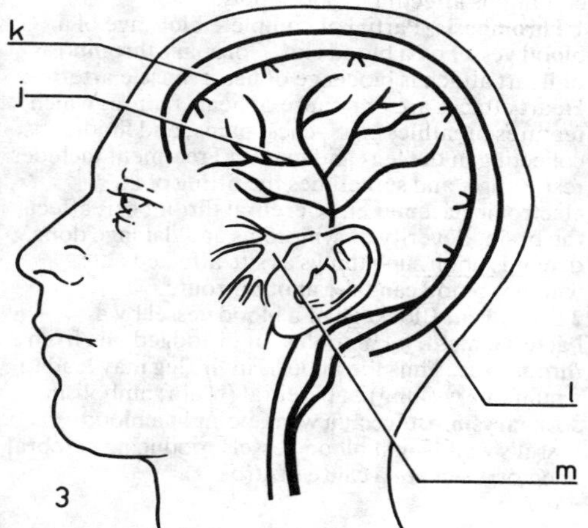

Circulatory problems

Problems include disorders of the blood (eg haemophilia, sickle-cell anaemia, and thalassemia), the heart (eg congenital defects and heart failure), and the blood vessels (eg blocked or burst blood vessels and varicose veins). Surgery or other treatments help several conditions affecting the heart and arteries.

Diagrams show common causes of serious conditions affecting blood supply.

1 Thrombosis. Partial or complete blockage of a blood vessel by a blood clot. Coronary thrombosis or heart attack is blockage of heart muscle arteries. Heart attacks are one cause of heart failure, which features breathlessness, chest pains, and fluid collecting in the legs and lungs. (Treatment includes rest, drugs, and sometimes the fitting of an electronic pacemaker.) Cerebral thrombosis affects the brain. Severity of symptoms and damage done depends upon such things as site affected and whether blood can take another route.

2 Embolism. Blockage of a blood vessel by a bacterial mass, fat globules, or dislodged bits from a thrombosis. Thus thrombosis in the leg may lead to a pulmonary (lung) or cerebral (brain) embolism.

3 Aneurysm. Bulge at a weak point in a blood vessel's wall. Burst blood vessels producing cerebral haemorrhage are a cause of strokes.

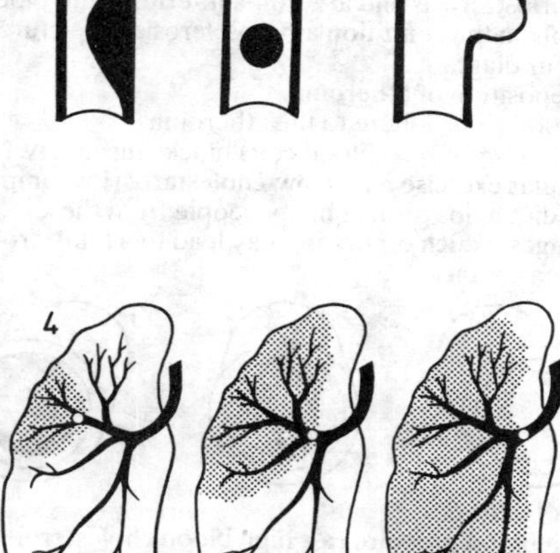

4 Infarction. Death of living tissue deprived of blood by embolism or thrombosis. Diagrams show different amounts of lung affected by pulmonary embolisms at different sites.

Aging arteries

With age, artery walls thicken and harden, a process called arteriosclerosis. Atheroma, deposition of a cholesterol-rich fatty deposit occurs on artery walls. Arteriosclerosis and atheroma interfere with blood supply in the condition atherosclerosis, as pictured in four diagrams.

1 Deposition of atheroma.

2 Blood clots adhere to the atheroma.

3 A big thrombus (blood clot) blocks the artery.

Regular exercise and a low-cholesterol (low-animal-fat) diet helps protect many people from these changes, which otherwise may lead to a fatal stroke or heart attack.

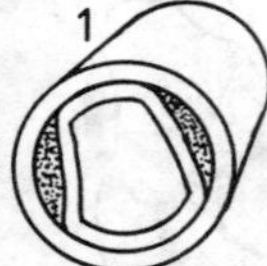

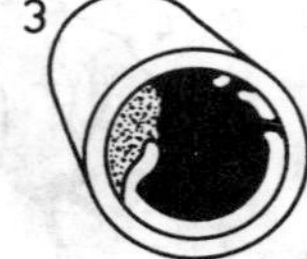

Risk factors

High blood pressure (**a**), high blood cholesterol level (**b**), and cigarette smoking (**c**) are normally the three main risk factors contributing to heart attack and angina pectoris (chest pain caused by the heart's inability to step up blood supply). Bar diagrams relate risk factors to risk of heart disease in three age groups. Bars marked (**o**) represent no risk factors. The risk can often be reduced by exercising, reducing body fat, reducing salt intake, and eating less animal fat.

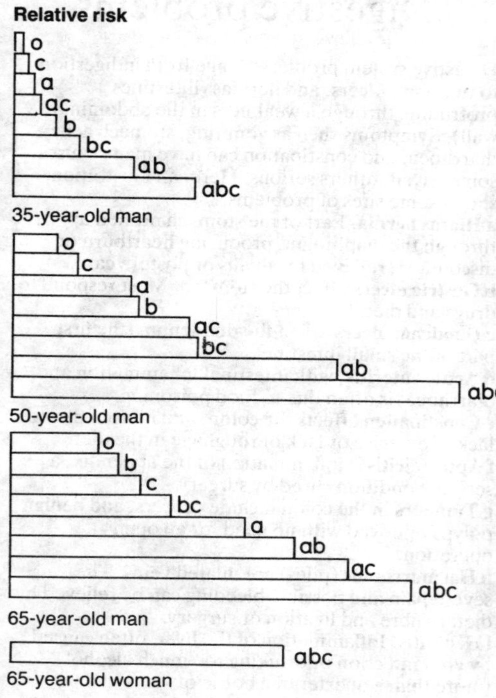
Relative risk
o
c
a
ac
b
bc
ab
abc
35-year-old man
o
c
a
b
ac
bc
ab
abc
50-year-old man
o
b
c
bc
a
ab
ac
abc
65-year-old man
abc
65-year-old woman

Digestive problems

Digestive system problems range from indigestion to tumours, ulcers, and hernias (intestines protruding through a weakness in the abdominal wall). Symptoms such as vomiting, stomach ache, diarrhoea, and constipation can have many causes, some trivial, others serious. Here, an illustration shows some sites of problems.

a **Hiatus hernia**. Part of the stomach pushed up through the diaphragm, producing heartburn or discomfort, relieved by alkalis or posture care.

b **Gastric ulcers** affect the stomach. Most respond to drugs and diet.

c **Duodenal ulcers** affect the duodenum (the first part of the small intestine).

d **Acute enteritis**, with intestinal inflammation and diarrhoea, is often due to food poisoning.

e **Constipation** affects the colon, and is often due to lack of exercise or lack of roughage in the diet.

f **Appendicitis** is inflammation of the appendix, a serious condition cured by surgery.

g **Tumours** in the colon include cancers, and benign polyps removed with no need for an open operation.

h **Haemorrhoids** (piles) are dilated veins. The severe pain and possible bleeding can be relieved by dietary fibre and ligation or surgery.

i **Hepatitis**. Inflammation of the liver, often caused by viral infection or drinking too much alcohol (more than a quarter of a bottle of spirits a day),

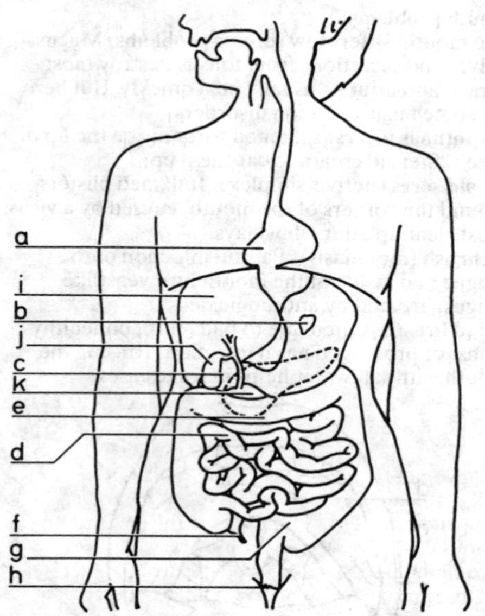

leading to serious liver damage called cirrhosis.
j Cholecystitis. Inflammation of the gall bladder, usually caused by gallstones, which can be removed.
k Pancreatitis. Inflammation of the pancreas, sometimes due to gallstones. Medical help is needed.

Mouth problems

The mouth suffers few serious problems. Mucus, saliva, and secretions from tonsils destroy most germs, and injuries usually heal quickly. But here are some fairly common disorders.

a Aphthous ulcers. Inflamed sores inside the lip or cheek. Steroid creams clear them up.

b Cold sores (herpes simplex). Inflamed blisters around the corners of the mouth, caused by a virus. Most clear up after a few days.

c Thrush (moniliasis). Painful infection of the tongue and inside of the mouth by a yeastlike fungus. Treated by antifungicides.

d Bad breath. Often due to bad teeth, unhealthy gums, or prolonged nasal infection. Rinsing the mouth with salt water helps in some cases.

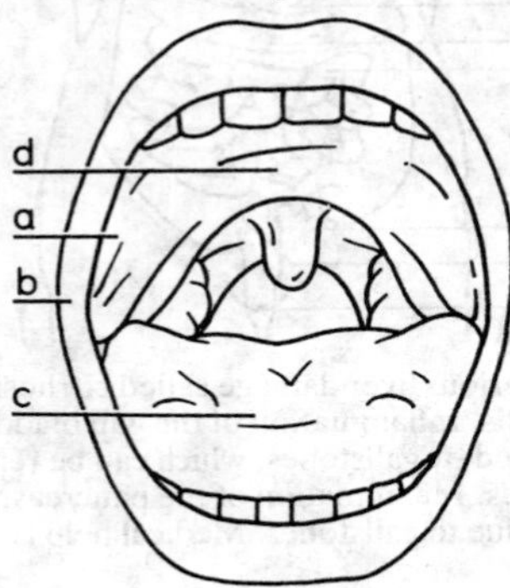

Tooth decay

Unattended surface tooth decay can cause progressive damage, as in these pictured teeth.

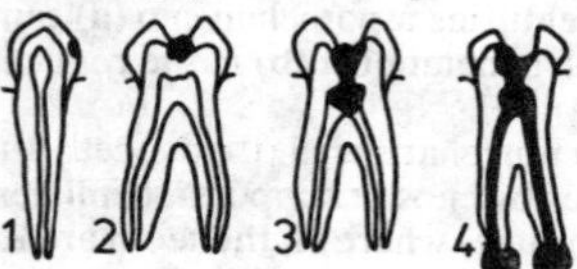

1 Incisor with decayed spot.
2 Molar with decay penetrating enamel and dentine.
3 Molar with decay penetrating to the pulp.
4 Molar with decay penetrating to the roots.

Dentists drill out decayed matter and replace with a lining of chemical cement, usually, an amalgam of several metals or translucent silicate cement.

Gum disorders

Eating only soft food, brushing teeth inefficiently, and other factors can cause gum disorders. Untreated, these may enlarge the sockets holding teeth (**a–d**) until teeth loosen and fall out. Improving oral hygiene and diet can reduce the risk of gum decay. Treatments include antiseptic mouthwashes, antibiotics, and even surgery of diseased gums.

Tooth replacement
Dentists can replace parts of teeth and groups of teeth as pictured here.
1 Crown, featuring a porcelain cap (**a**) cemented to a tooth with a metal post (**b**) in the root canal.
2 Bridge.
3 Partial denture: artificial plastic teeth attached to natural ones by clips or supports. (Full dentures can be made for jaws where all the teeth are lost.)

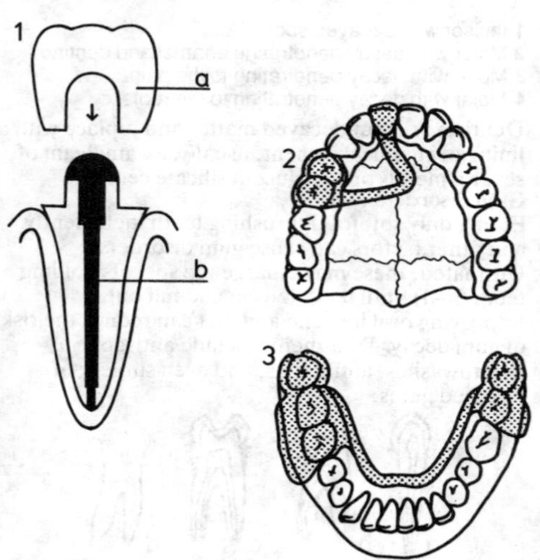

Respiratory disorders

Nasal passages and sinuses (air-filled cavities) suffer infections and other problems.

1 Nasal passages

a Common cold. Running and maybe blocked nose, and loss of sense of smell, due to a viral infection. Usually clearing up after a few days.

b Hay fever. Swollen mucous membranes of nose and eyes, with watery discharge and sneezing. Due to allergic reaction, relieved by antihistamine drugs.

c Nose bleeds. Caused by a ruptured blood vessel in the nose, usually stopped by pinching the nostrils. Persistent nosebleed calls for medical aid.

d Polyps. Benign tumours partly blocking nasal passages, and removed by surgery.

e Rhinitis. Inflammation of nasal membranes caused by colds or hay fever.

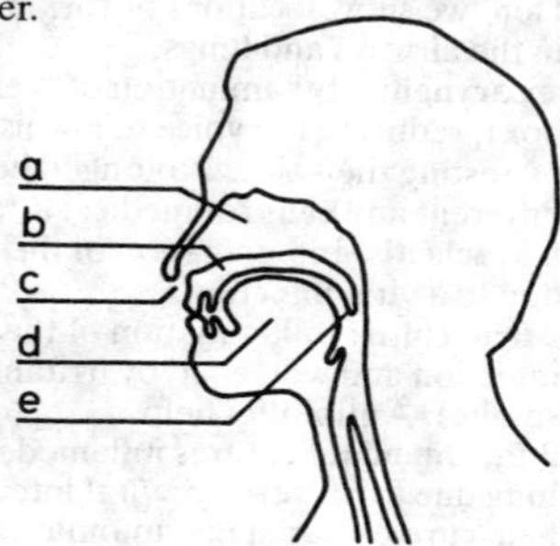

a Nasal cavity
b Hard palate
c Nostril
d Tongue
e Uvula

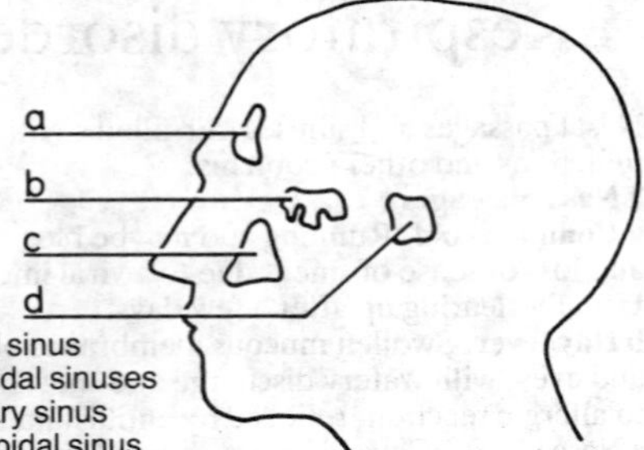

a Frontal sinus
b Ethmoidal sinuses
c Maxillary sinus
d Sphenoidal sinus

2 Sinuses
Sinusitis. Inflammation causing headaches and pain in cheekbones. Drugs help and minor surgery improves the more intractable conditions.

Lung and vocal disorders
Here we show locations of various problems arising in the airways and lungs.

a Laryngitis. Inflammation of the larynx (voice box), reducing the voice to a whisper, and treated by resting the voice. Prolonged hoarseness is different and calls for medical attention.

b Tracheitis. Inflammation of the trachea, usually due to a viral infection.

c Bronchitis. Inflammation of the bronchi, due to infection and worsened by irritants (eg cigarette smoke). Antibiotics help.

d Pneumonia. Features inflamed, fluid-filled areas of lung due to bacterial or viral infection. Antibiotics help cure bacterial pneumonia.

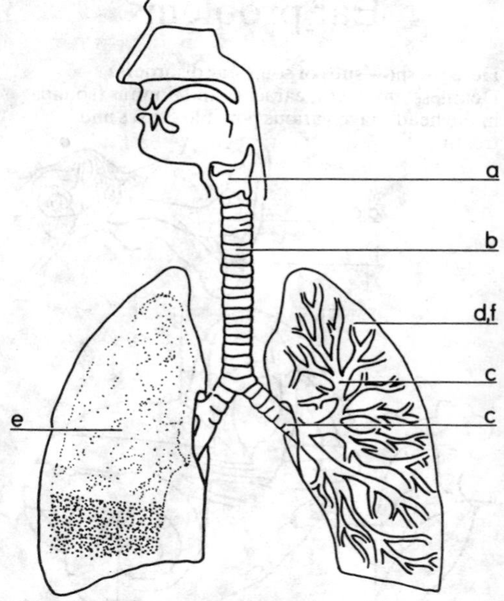

e Pleurisy. Inflammation of the pleura (the membrane around the lungs), a sometimes painful condition accompanying lung inflammation.
f Tuberculosis of the lung. Lung damage caused by tuberculosis bacteria. Treated by antibiotics.

Ear problems

Here we show sites of some ear disorders. Deafness, dizziness, earache, and tinnitus (sounds in the head) have various possible causes and treatments.

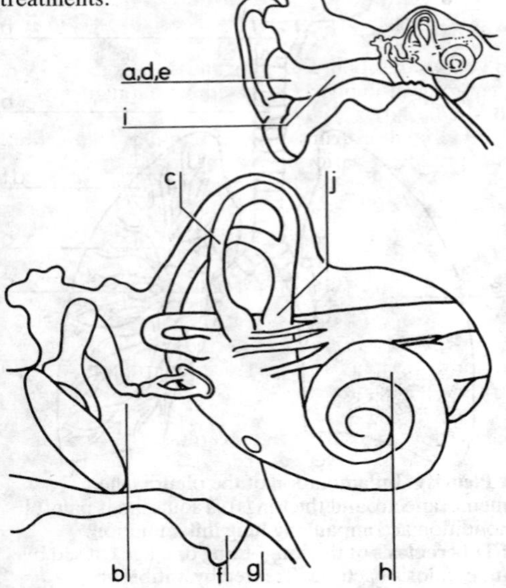

A Outer ear
a Blockage. Ear wax or foreign bodies can cause deafness, relieved by a doctor syringing the ear with warm water and/or an agent that dissolves wax.
b Discharge from the ear is often due to otitis externa or fungus infection.
c Otitis externa. Infection, inflammation, and maybe earache due often to boils needing medical help.
d Fungus infection. Irritation and discharge requiring antibiotic and antiseptic treatment.
B Middle ear
e Perforated eardrum. Caused by injury or infection and producing various problems including conduction deafness, helped by a hearing aid.
f Otitis media. Bacterial infection, maybe with pain and pus perforating the eardrum. Treated with antibiotic drugs.
g Mastoiditis. Painful inflammation of the mastoid bone, a potentially serious condition that can be treated by antibiotics or surgery.
h Otosclerosis. Bone overgrowth in the oval window, stopping airborne sound vibrations reaching the inner ear. Usually treatable by surgery.
C Inner ear
i Perceptive (sensorineural) **deafness**. Deafness due to inner ear or nerve damage. Often helped by a carefully chosen hearing aid.
j Menière's disease. Dizziness attacks, deafness, and head noises. Treatments include various drugs.

Eye problems

Common eye problems include small objects lodged in front of the eye, styes, and conjunctivitis. These may need medical help, but usually respond to simple home treatment.

a Small objects are usually removed by blinking, pulling the upper eyelid over the lower eyelid, or using the corner of a handkerchief.

b A stye is an infected, inflamed sebaceous gland around an eyelash, usually treated by removing the eyelash and bathing the eye in hot water.

c Conjunctivitis is inflammation of the conjunctiva (membrane lining the eyelid), due to infection or irritation. Treatment may involve antibiotics or removing the irritant.

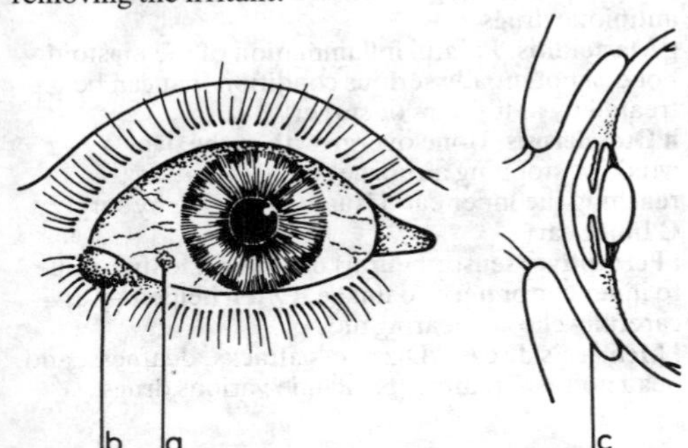

Sight defects

Faulty focusing by the eye produces nearsightedness (short sight) or farsightedness (long sight). Both can be treated by spectacles or contact lenses. (Special lenses may be needed for astigmatism, a condition where the eye cannot focus both horizontally and vertically.)

1a Nearsightedness (myopia): Light rays from a distant object focus in front of the retina
1b A concave lens corrects nearsightedness.
2a Farsightedness (hypermetropia): Light rays from a nearby object focus behind the retina.
2b A convex lens corrects farsightedness.

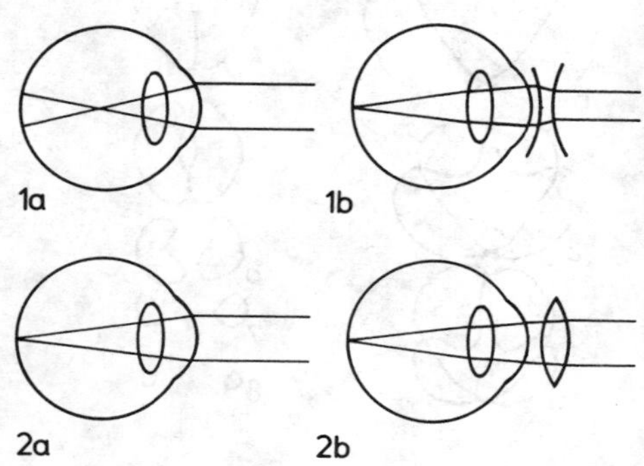

Blindness

Blindness can be total or partial. Illustrations **1–8** show gradual loss of field of vision in a form of progressive blindness.

Blindness may be due to one of a number of causes affecting different parts of the eye. Thus keratitis and cataract respectively make the cornea and lens opaque. Retinitis, retinopathy, retinal detachment, and glaucoma affect sensory cells at the back of the eye. Some forms of blindness (eg glaucoma) can be prevented, some others (eg cataract) treated.

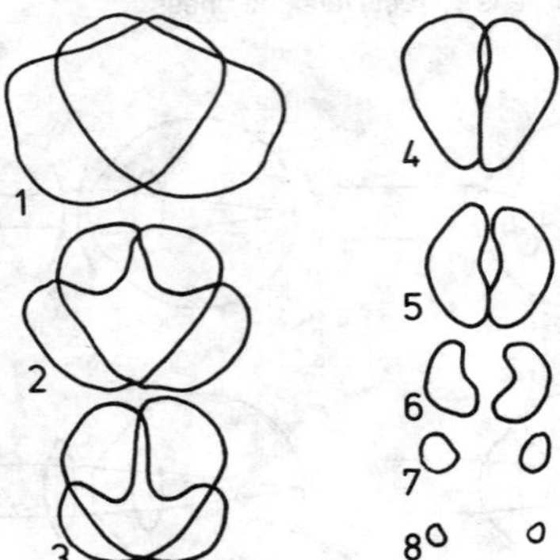

Skin and hair problems

Hair loss

Hair loss from the head can come with mental stress or physical problems from scars and burns to skin disease or serious anaemia. But the usual form is progressive baldness (**1–5**) seen in middle-aged and older men. This is due to the combination of a male hormone with hereditary aging factors. Most men and women suffer from some hair loss as they age. There is no known cure or way of slowing down the process, though some claim benefit from hair transplants.

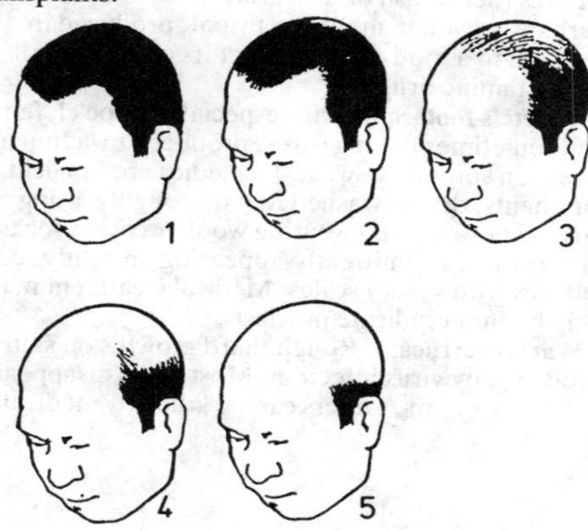

Skin and hair problems

Here we show some sites of common skin disorders.
a Acne. Inflamed boils, commonest at puberty. Treatments include medicines and sunlight.
b Boils. Painful lumps discharging pus. Some need medical treatment. Most clear up unaided.
c Dermatitis. Inflammation with blistering and flaking skin due to irritants, or allergic reaction to normally non-irritant substances. (Sometimes confused with atopic eczema.) Lotions help and sufferers should avoid irritant substances.
d Hives (nettlerash or urticaria). Itchy red weals and perhaps a swollen mouth or throat, produced in reaction to a food or drug. Doctors often prescribe antihistamine drugs.
e Athlete's foot. Split skin (especially in toe clefts) and sometimes flaking sores, produced by a fungus infection spread by sweat. Remedies are fungicidal ointments, drying washed feet thoroughly, using dusting powder, and wearing wool or cotton socks.
f Psoriasis. Intermittently-appearing unsightly red patches with silvery scales. Medical treatment may help but not eradicate psoriasis.
g Warts (verrucas): Rough, hard growths on skin produced by virus infection. Most warts disappear within two years. Others can be killed by medical treatment.

h Cold sores (herpes simplex) involve reddened skin where small blisters burst to produce a crust on lips, and sometimes on the cheeks and genitals. Lotions may relieve irritation but the crust usually falls off in about a week.

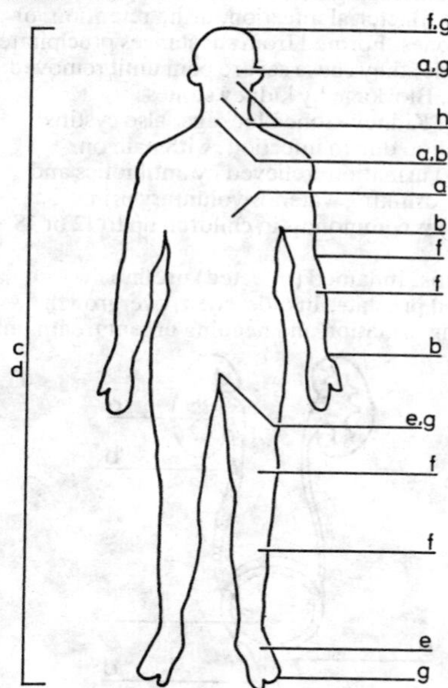

Urinary disorders

Each part of the urinary system is liable to problems, including those we list below.
a Kidneys. Bacterial infection, urine retention, or kidney stones. Formed from substances precipitated out of urine, they cause severe pain until removed.
b Ureters. Blockage by kidney stones.
c Bladder. Kidney-stone blockage, also cystitis: inflammation due to infection, with pain on (frequent) urination, relieved by antibiotics and copiously drinking water. Involuntary urination (enuresis) is commonest in children up to 12 or 18 months.
d Urethritis. Inflamed (infected) urethra.
e Enlarged prostate. In older men, overgrowth preventing urination and needing urgent treatment.

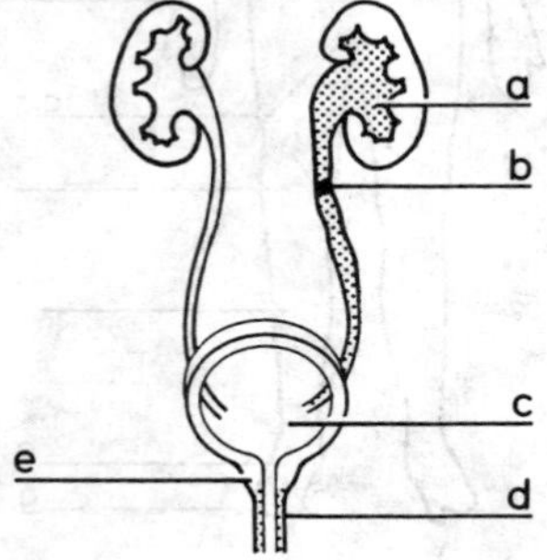

Hormone problems

Underactive or overactive endocrine glands produce various hormonal diseases. Doctors combat some by artificially adjusting hormone balance.

a Pituitary gland malfunction can produce growth abnormalities creating dwarfs and giants.

b Thyroid gland malfunction can cause goitre (an enlarged thyroid gland) and slow down or speed up the body's metabolism.

c Pancreas malfunction (inability to manufacture insulin) produces diabetes: a condition where the body cannot use sugar.

d Adrenal glands' malfunction causes Addison's disease, with weakness and weight loss.

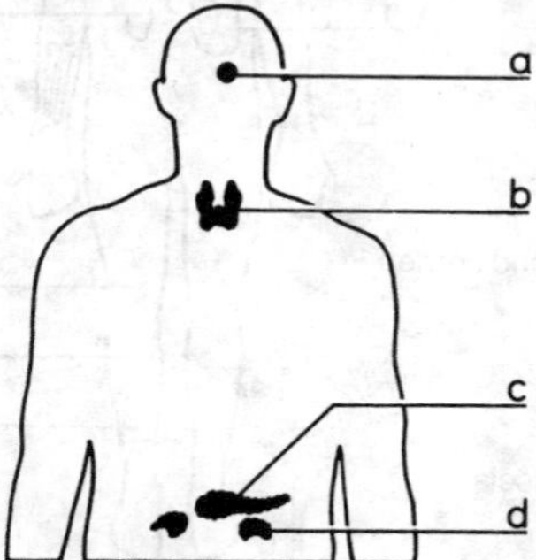

Organ transplants

Surgeons can now graft skin from one part of a body to another, and replace certain diseased or damaged organs with healthy counterparts from dead or living donors. Such biological transplants can often prolong life or repair fire-ravaged hands and faces. On a human outline we indicate some of the best-known items that have been treated in this way.

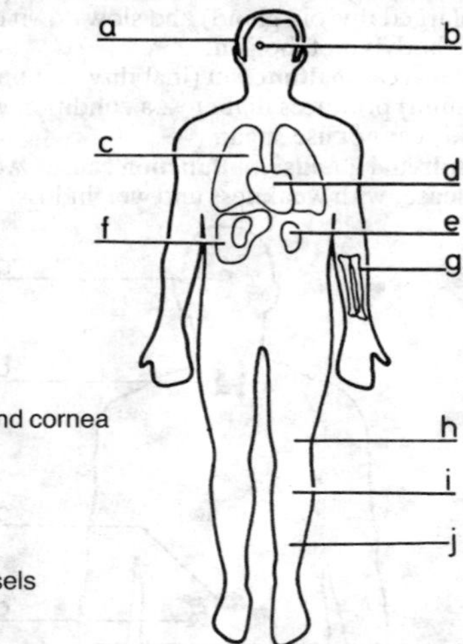

a Hair
b Eye lens and cornea
c Lungs
d Heart
e Kidneys
f Liver
g Bones
h Blood vessels
i Blood
j Skin

Spare parts
Plastics, metals, and other substitutes for flesh and bone figure in a number of prostheses (artificial body parts), replacing items damaged or destroyed by disease or injury.
We indicate a number of these items on a human outline.

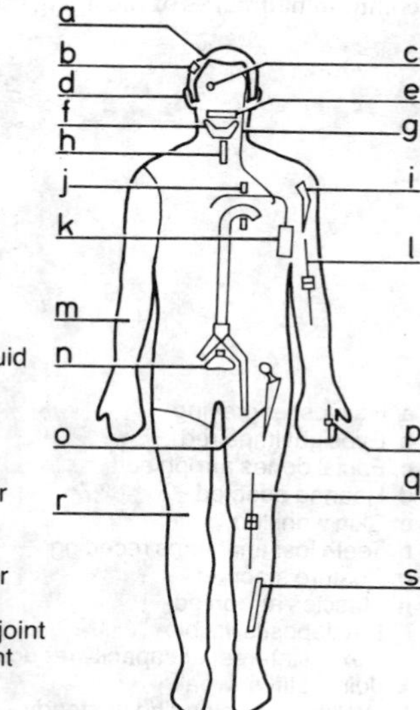

- **a** False hair
- **b** Plate in the skull
- **c** Artificial cornea
- **d** Artificial ear
- **e** False teeth
- **f** False jaw
- **g** Cerebrospinal fluid drain
- **h** Artificial larynx
- **i** Shoulder joint
- **j** Heart valves
- **k** Heart pacemaker
- **l** Elbow joint
- **m** Artificial arm
- **n** Bladder simulator
- **o** Artificial hip joint
- **p** Artificial knuckle joint
- **q** Artificial knee joint
- **r** Artificial leg
- **s** Metal plate

Visible changes after 60

Aging starts in the late or middle 20s, and becomes noticeable by the 40s. By 60 physical changes are plainly visible as bones, joints, teeth, muscles, skin, and hair deteriorate. Here, labelled items show common hallmarks of the aging body.

a Hair lost or greying
b Eyesight impaired
c Facial bones atrophied
d Hearing affected
e Skin wrinkled
f Teeth lost and gums receding
g Posture stooped
h Muscles atrophied
i Fat deposits visible
j Sexual interest or capacity reduced
k Joints stiff or weak
l Walking and standing unsteady

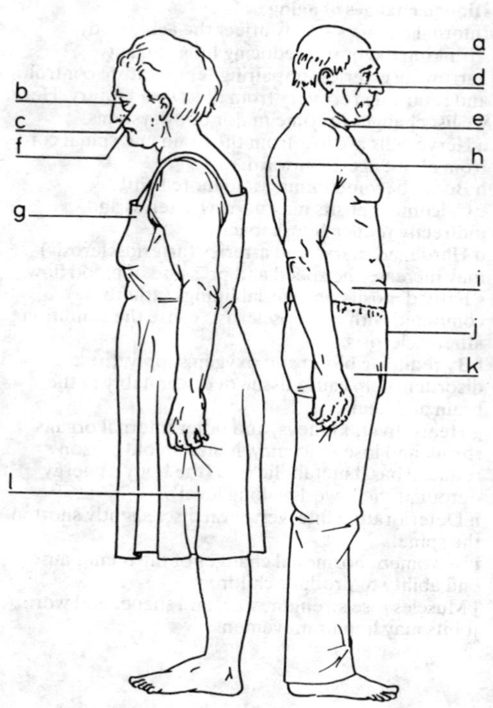
a
d
b
c
e
f
h
g
i
j
k
l

Hidden changes of aging

Internal changes slowly affect the aging body, shrinking the brain, reducing lung capacity, narrowing arteries, impairing temperature control, and retarding recovery from illness and injury. Here we list changes to some major body systems.

a Nerve cells are lost from the brain and spinal cord from about age 25 onward.

b Bones become thinner and more brittle.

c Calcium deposits may narrow arteries and indirectly reduce lung capacity.

d Hardened, narrowed arteries (arteriosclerosis) may increase the speed and pressure of blood flow.

e Fatty deposits on arterial linings (atheroma) combined with arteriosclerosis cause the condition atherosclerosis.

f By reducing blood and oxygen supply, these disorders help cause tissue decay, notably in the brain and heart.

g Heart, liver, kidneys, and other internal organs shrink and lose efficiency, hence an old person's reduced basal metabolic rate (the body's energy output at the lowest waking level).

h Deteriorating intervertebral discs slightly shorten the spine.

i In women, hormonal changes of the menopause end ability to produce children.

j Muscles lose strength, size, and shape, and worn joints may impair movement.

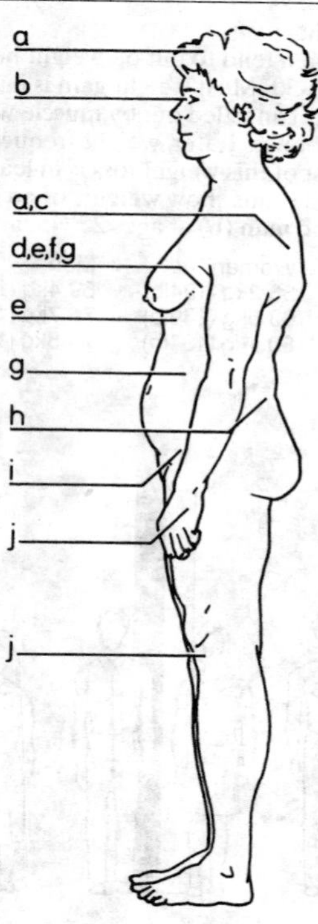
a
b
a,c
d,e,f,g
e
g
h
i
j
j

Age and weight
Men and women tend to put on weight between ages 25 and 45-50. Most weight gain is in fat, though it is sometimes cancelled out by muscle wastage and lightening of bones. Later, weight frequently declines. Most of this weight loss is in lean tissue. Here three diagrams show weights of an average woman (**a**) and man (**b**) at ages 25, 45, and 65.

	Woman	Man
1 At age 25	56.2kg (124lb)	69.4kg (153lb)
2 At age 45	63.0kg (139lb)	76.7kg (173lb)
3 At age 65	60.7kg (134lb)	74.5kg (164lb)

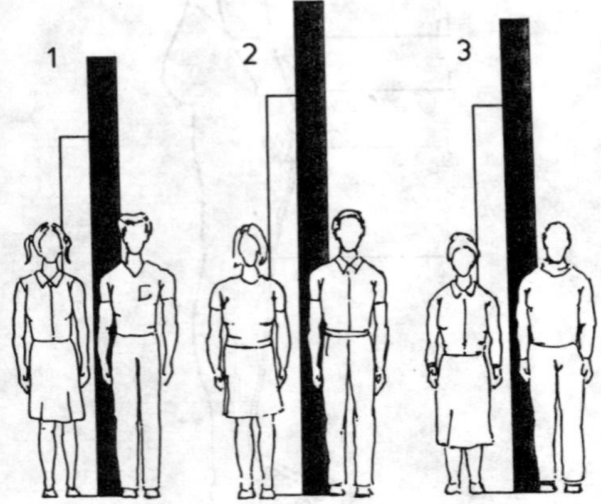

Declining abilities

The chart below shows proportions of certain physical and mental abilities (**A**) retained and (**B**) lost by age 75.

Physical abilities:

1 Speed at which nerves transmit signals
2 Biceps circumference
3 Grip persistence
4 Maximum rate of work
5 Visual acuity at 6m (20ft)
6 Hearing
7 Reaction time
8 Hand grip
9 Maximum breathing rate
10 Maximum work rate (short term)

Mental abilities:

11 Defining words
12 General knowledge
13 Verbal intelligence
14 Commonsense understanding
15 Arithmetic
16 Non-verbal intelligence
17 Intellectual efficiency

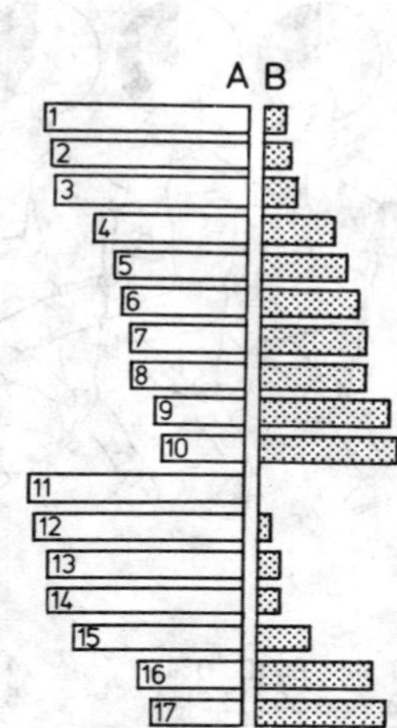

Decline in speed

Most kinds of physical performance reach their peak in your mid-20s and then decline as you age. Here we give the percentages of a lifetime's peak speed lost by a middle-distance runner at various ages from 60 to 80.

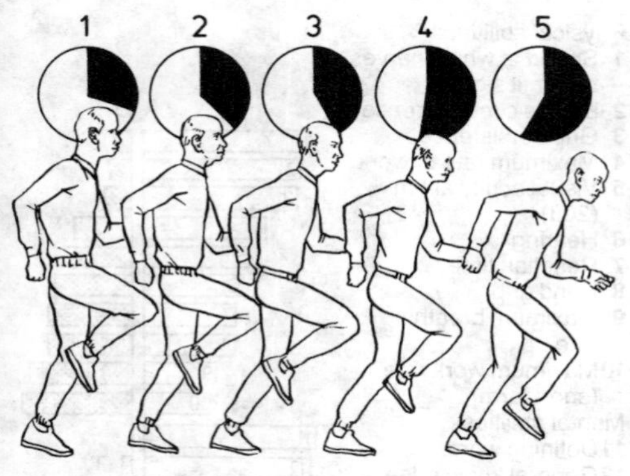

1 Age 60 (28.0%)
2 Age 65 (35.3%)
3 Age 70 (42.8%)
4 Age 75 (50.5%)
5 Age 80 (58.3%)

Heart–lung output
Two graphs contrast cardiac output (**1**) and stroke volume (**2**) in young men and men aged 65. The higher a line, the greater the cardiac output in litres per minute and the higher the stroke volume in millilitres. The farther right a line extends the greater is oxygen consumption in litres per minute. Old men reach peak cardiac output when doing less work than young men. In old men increasing effort reduces stroke volume.

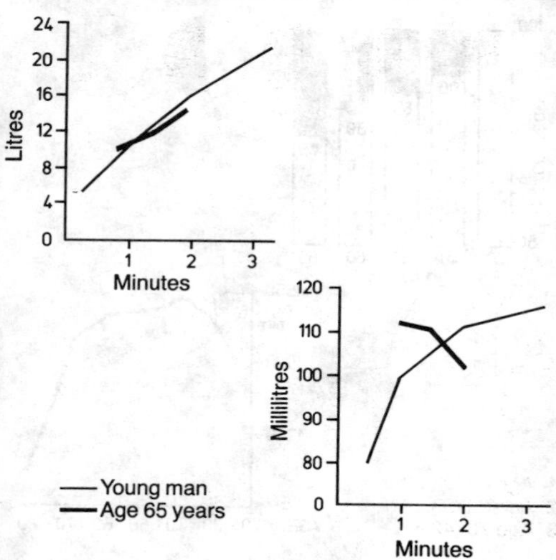

Muscle strength

A bar diagram and a graph show how muscle strength alters with age.

1 Decline in muscular strength after a peak in the late 20s. Numbers on bars show percentages of muscular strength retained at different ages.

2 Decline in medium cranking rates (kg-m/min) for men aged 25 to 80. Strength of arms and shoulders reaches a peak between ages 30 and 40, stays high until 60, and falls steeply after age 65.

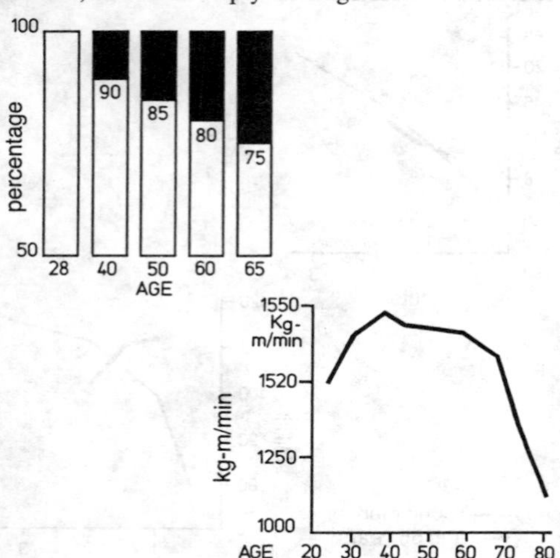

Bone loss
Bones lose material and fractures grow more likely as we age, as these two graphs reveal.
1 Percentage bone and mineral loss in women and men in their 20s and older. Bone loss rises sharply by the 60s, and older women tend to suffer more bone loss than older men.
2 Percentage increase in fractures occurring in women and men in their 20s and older. Fractures increase sharply by the mid-60s. Again women suffer more bone breakages than men.

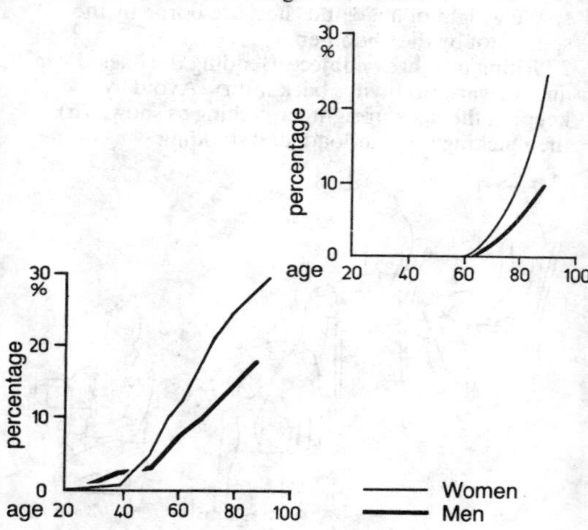

Keeping age at bay

Commonsense measures such as proper posture and regular simple exercises can guard against the physical problems of aging.

Posture after 40

Posture care is important in preventing injury to aging muscles, bones, and joints.

1 Sitting. Slouching (**a**) with bent back and bottom forward sets up strain. Avoid by sitting upright (**b**), so the weight of head and chest are borne by the spine, not by the abdomen.

2 Picking up a heavy object. Bending the back down and forward (**a**) invites back injury. Avoid by keeping the back upright, crouching as shown (**b**), then picking up your load, and standing.

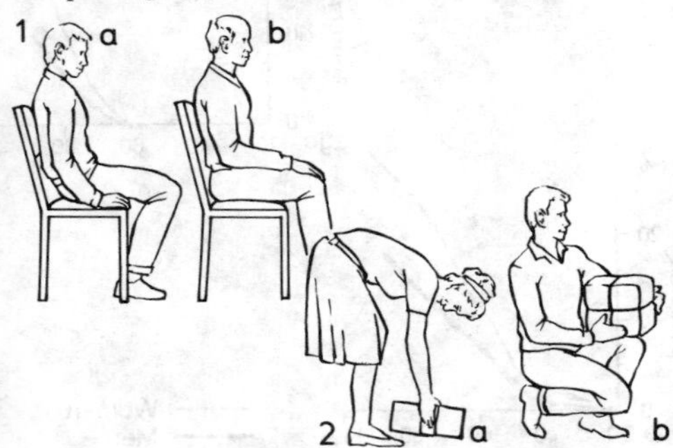

3 Pushing a heavy object. In pushing with the back, shoulders, or arms, exert pressure by bending and then straightening the legs.

Staying mobile

Exercising joints helps fend off the stiffness that restricts joint movements as we age. Here we show items from a few selected exercises that many older people find beneficial to the joints of the neck, arms, hands, trunk, legs, and feet. People should exercise regularly and gradually increase the number of exercises they attempt. (For the active older person, doctors also advise regular walking or other appropriate heart–lung exercise.)

1 Turn the head left, then right. Then let it drop forwards and backwards.
2 Raise arms above the head. Then raise one arm while lowering the other, and alternate.
3 Stretch arms and hands forward, hands palm down. Make fists, then spread your fingers. (You can do this and the previous exercise in bed.)
4 Standing with legs apart, with the right hand try touching your left foot. Then use the left hand to try to touch the right foot.

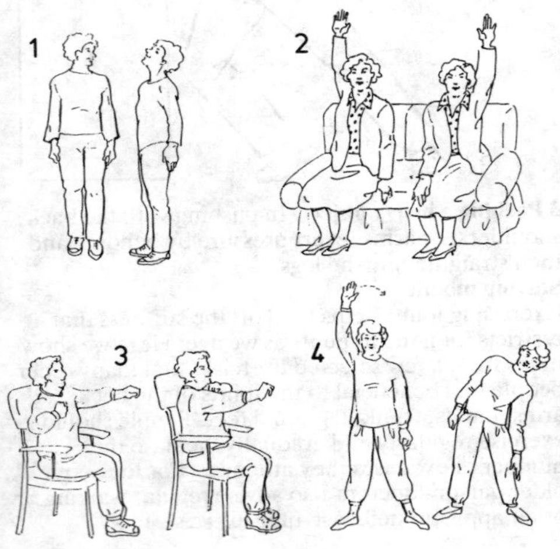

5 Lie on your back with arms stretched out behind your head. Then lift your left leg and bring the right arm forward as if to touch the leg. Slowly lower leg and arm. Then repeat with the right leg and left arm.
6 Standing relaxed, raise your heels. Then rock back to stand on your heels.
7 Standing with feet flat on the ground, turn toes in and heels out, and raise heels. Then turn heels in and toes out, raising toes.

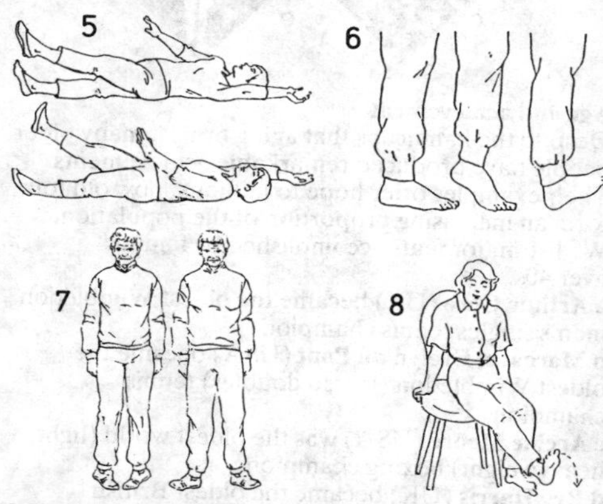

8 Sitting on a chair, extend your right leg. With its foot just off the ground, wriggle the toes. Repeat this exercise with your left foot.

Age and achievement
Despite the handicaps that aging brings, many older people have produced remarkable achievements. Their examples offer hope to millions, now old folk form an increasing proportion of the population. We list major feats accomplished by famous over 40s.

a Arthur Gore (UK) became the oldest Wimbledon men's singles tennis champion.

b Margaret Evelyn du Pont (USA) became the oldest Wimbledon (mixed doubles) tennis champion.

c Archie Moore (USA) was the oldest world (light heavyweight) boxing champion.

d Reg Harris (UK) became the oldest British national sprint cycling champion.

e Albert Rayner (UK) broke the world record for skipping in 10 seconds.

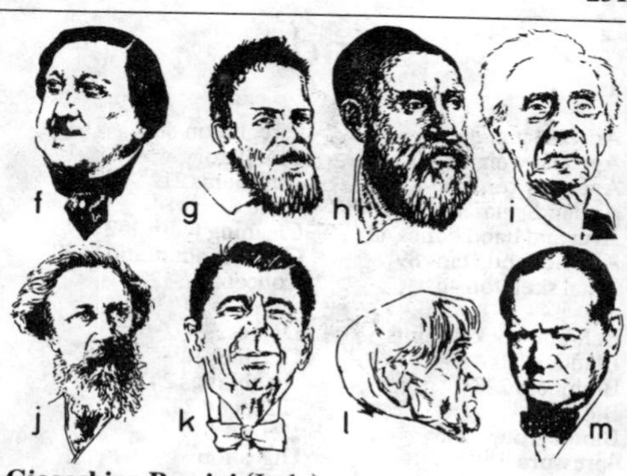

f Gioacchino Rossini (Italy) wrote the *Petite Messe Solenelle* at age 72.
g Galileo Galilei (Italy) produced his final discoveries in astronomy at age 73.
h Titian (Italy) died at 86, painting his *Pièta*.
i Bertrand Russell (UK) released his autobiography at age 97.
j Nikolaevich Tolstoy (Russia) wrote the short story *Alesha goryok* at age 77.
k Ronald Reagan (USA) became the president of the United States at age 70.
l Ralph Vaughan Williams (UK) produced his *9th Symphony* at age 85.
m Sir Winston Churchill (UK) resigned as British premier at age 80.

Index